OMAR

Rose Bavistock is a spinster of enlightened views, a passionate animal lover. Omar, "a bandersnatch," comes to her as a pet: he is a rare mammal, small in size, furry to the touch, and volatile in temperament. Under Miss Bavistock's gentle eye, he slowly reveals singular capacities, the least of which is speech.

Venit, vidit, dixit . . . after arriving, surveying the scene, and, with some reluctance, admitting his ability to speak English at least as fluently as his owner, "indeed more grammatically," he enters upon his public life—and there he conquers.

When Omar at last returns to a domestic life in the obscurity of his native Hyrcanian woods, he has made an impression upon the reader, with his urbane, even cynical, but wholly animal character, out of all proportion to the modest aims of this delightfully idiosyncratic fantasy.

The Haileybury Buildings
Desert Hawk
The Art of Botanical Illustration
Tulipomania
Black Sunrise
Sweet Roman Hand
Japanese Colour Prints
Flower Drawings of Georg Dionysius Ehret
Pietro's Pilgrimage
Sebastiano
Great Flower Books (with Sacheverell Sitwell)
A Persian Spring
Gerard von Spaendonck
Lady Muriel
Of Flowers and a Village
Cockerell
Isfahan

OMAR

A Fantasy for Animal Lovers
by WILFRID BLUNT

with illustrations by John Verney

Doubleday & Company, Inc., Garden City, New York
1968

To
Christopher & Elisabeth

Library of Congress Catalog Card Number 68–22524
First published in 1966
by Chapman & Hall, Ltd.
11 New Fetter Lane, London E.C.4
Copyright © 1966 by Wilfrid Blunt
All Rights Reserved
Printed in the United States of America
First Edition in the United States of America

Author's Preface

Anyone who writes a work of fiction in the first person will find himself, sooner or later, identified by many of his readers with the "I" of his story. After the publication of my *Of Flowers and a Village* I learned that I was believed by some to hold all the heretical opinions uttered by its hero, Wilfrid Sharp, although I had expressly stated in the Preface that this was not so.

Miss Rose Bavistock, the "I" of *Omar,* and Omar himself who might perhaps be described as its hero, express many views that I consider outrageous or even downright ludicrous (though in certain matters I admit that I am in full agreement with both of them). I was, for example, distressed to find one or other of them sometimes poking mild fun at such revered institutions as the Papacy or the Press; but what could I do about it? I particularly wish to dissociate myself from their criticism of the London Zoological Gardens, which I have no doubt will be run in the future as admirably as they are now.

I am extremely grateful to Mr. Raef Payne for suggesting the Tree Hyrax as the appropriate animal on which to base my mythical Bandersnatch, and to Mr. Gavin Maxwell for information about its character and behaviour; to Sir John Verney for his delightful illustrations; to Mrs. Arthur Harrison and others who gave me advice and criticism or who read the proofs; and once again to Miss Violet Thayre for her fine typing.

W. J. W. B.

The Watts Gallery
Compton, Guildford
19th April 1966

Contents

I think I could turn and live with animals, they're so
                    placid and self-contain'd,
I stand and look at them long and long.

They do not sweat and whine about their condition,
They do not lie awake in the dark and weep for
                              their sins,
They do not make me sick discussing their duty to
                              God,
Not one is dissatisfied, not one is demented with the
                    mania of owning things,
Not one kneels to another, nor to his kind that lived
                    thousands of years ago,
Not one is respectable or unhappy over the whole
                              earth . . .

Walt Whitman, "Song of Myself," LEAVES OF GRASS

Part I
VENIT

I

Beware the Jabberwock, my son!
The jaws that bite, the claws that catch!
Beware the Jubjub bird, and shun
The frumious Bandersnatch!

Alice through the Looking-Glass

Let me introduce myself.

My name is Rose Bavistock. I am a spinster, now in my middle fifties; but this story begins five years ago. My mother died when I was a child. I had no brother or sister, and I had lived all my life—but for several wretched years at a boarding-school—with my father in Disbourne, a small and rather isolated village about four miles from Haslemere. Father had inherited enough money to make it unnecessary for him to earn his living. This was probably just as well: he was a scholar and a recluse, and would have been quite unsuited to any career except perhaps that of a don or a country parson. He did, in fact, sometimes speak of ordination, but the effort involved always proved too great.

Father was a voracious reader—and reading is a taste that I suppose I inherited from him. He spent most of his day, and often half the night, among his books; but every afternoon, and whatever the weather, he would go for a long walk, generally alone but occasionally with the Rector, a man named Ralph Aylmer. A scholar and for many years a widower like himself, Aylmer was almost his only friend in Disbourne, indeed almost his only friend in the world; and his quite unexpected remarriage to a rather gushing middle-aged local spinster had been, I believe, a great blow to Father.

Ever since I first remember him, Father had always been on the point of producing a monumental work on the Early Christian Church; at the time of his death it still remained unfinished. It sounds rather awful to say it, but he was a bore with a one-track mind. Mark Twain, when he was in Rome, deplored that he was given "Michael Angelo for breakfast—for luncheon—for tea—for supper—for between meals"; Mother did not want the Early Christian Church in that concentration either, but she got it none the less. Or so I imagine; for I was only five when she died, and I can remember little more of her than her big sad eyes. As for me, I eventually made it clear to Father that I was not going to stand for his tedious regurgitations of Eusebius, or whatever he was engrossed in at the moment, at every meal; so we sat opposite one another in silence, each with a book propped on a bookrest, while I attempted to swallow the unappetising food provided for us by what Father always called "our faithful Martha." Father was quite indifferent to what he ate.

This is the story of an animal, and I wish I could say that it was to be unfolded in some sun-spangled paradise of spume and waterfalls such as that in which Mr. Gavin Maxwell lived with and loved and was bitten by his enchanting otters. But my little drama opens and is largely played in a hideous Victorian house on the fringes of commutopia, half-smothered by that violet-coloured wisteria that ought never to be planted against red brick. The house was, however, easy to run; also we had four acres of ground, and this large garden gave me room to keep my pets without which I think I would have gone mad.

Father was as bored with me as I was with him. He used to say that he wished I had been a boy, by which I think he meant no more than that I would then have gone out into the world and troubled him no further. Father also once said that I looked like a horse (whereas I had always thought that I looked like Edith Sitwell). Though this was not intended as a compliment I took it as such, for animals are superior to man in almost every respect; remember that it was man, not the animals, whom God ejected from Paradise. And Madame Roland wrote, "Plus je vois les hommes, plus je respecte les chiens"; the brutality of man she was finally to realize to the full when she mounted the steps to the guillotine. I would rather have been an animal—*any* animal, even a toad—than a human being; perhaps, if my life has been good (or bad?) enough, I shall be reincarnated as a quadruped.

As far back as I can remember I had my pets. At first they were the obvious ones—white mice, an earwig or two, a toad, a bird ejected from an overcrowded nest or a "hospital case" with a broken wing; these aroused no parental opposition. Then I became more ambitious, and my pocket-money, which was generous, went on a marmo-set, and axolotl, or a pair of paradise whydahs. Father now became rather tiresome about it, and my position was weakened when the marmoset upset an ink-bottle over the rare Savile edition (1618) of Thomas Bradwardine's *De Causa Dei contra Pelagium*.

When I grew up and came into a small sum of money left me by my mother, I acquired—for Father could no longer very well prevent it—a succession of yet choicer animals, including at one time or another two leopard cubs, a young cheetah, a timber-wolf, an alligator, and an otter. For a while, inspired by the example of Dante Gabriel Rossetti, I had a wombat; but like him I was not successful in keeping her for long. There were also various dogs and cats. For my exotic pets, of which I seldom had more than two or perhaps three simultaneously, I had constructed at the bottom of the garden several enclosures, cages and pools to suit their varying needs.

These animals were my whole life.

I think it may have been Goethe who said, "It is not the steak that bestows the roses, but the onions." Of course I am a vegetarian, and it has always been a source of regret to me that the carnivores that I have kept have persistently refused to follow my example and forgo the flesh of animals. At first I attempted to feed my leopard cubs on nut-steaks that were visually indistinguishable from the genuine article; but they lost weight so rapidly that I had to give them food to which they had grown accustomed before they came to me. It was the same with my otter,

Tarquinia, who demanded fish in enormous quantities. In this, and perhaps only in this, are some "animals" inferior to some human beings.

It ought hardly to be necessary to mention that I am anti-bloodsport—or "field sport" as it is euphemistically called by those who indulge in it. I agree with Dr. Johnson that it is "very strange and very melancholy that the paucity of human pleasures should persuade us ever to call hunting one of them." "Sportsmen" are so retarded mentally that argument with them is simply time wasted; I prefer action. More than once I have attended meets of the Haslemere and tampered with the scent. This made me very unpopular in certain quarters; as it happens I couldn't care less, but in any case I would be proud to suffer in so good a cause.

At one time I belonged to three different societies for the abolition of vivisection, but I have now resigned from them all. Very regrettably, they seem to be principally concerned with trying to vivisect one another, and I sometimes wonder whether I ought not to found one of my own which had the interests of the animals really at heart. But if I did so, I would of course consider it my first duty to expose the corruption that exists elsewhere in the anti-vivisection world. Also I have now discovered that when I pare my finger-nails I am performing vivisection.

Is it not extraordinary that so many people who claim to love animals really only love the larger and more immediately engaging ones? A man who would never dream of torturing a dog, will go into his garden and spray his roses with Abol and sleep that night not a wink the less for the slow murders that he has committed. On what authority do we assume that God is a kind of American who cares for nothing that is not outsize? I have never intentionally taken the life of even the most irritating gnat—not even of the bed-bug that made my brief stay at Assisi so unpleasurable.

This brings me to the wonderful Jains. It is sometimes said that all foreigners are cruel to animals. Certainly I shall never again go to France or Italy, where I was so revolted by what I saw that I cut my holiday short and came straight back to England; what can be said in favour of France, where the law allows a man to torture an animal to his heart's content *so long as he does it in private?* The mere thought of Spain and its bull-fights nauseates me. But there are some notable exceptions: in Morocco, for example, there are (I have read) hospitals endowed by pious Muslim women for the support of superannuated storks; and in India there are the Jains. An Englishman named John Ovington, who was in Surat towards the close of the seventeenth century, describes a hospital that he visited there, established by the Jains for the care of bugs, fleas and other blood-sucking animals. Beggars were hired by the night as blood-donors; they were well strapped down on beds, and their bodies then made available to such vermin as happened to be in-patients at the time.

It is this absolutely consistent attitude of Jainism that so appeals to me. The Jains do not even clean their teeth, for fear of injuring living things. This is further than I am at present prepared to go; but since I first learnt of it, I have been cleaning mine only once a day. There is something very attractive, too, about the Jains' doctrine of

Syād-vāda, by which one may say "yes" and at the same time "no" to everything. In fact I think I might perhaps become a Jain, were it not that our climate is ill-suited to taking meals "sky-clad."

Among the many brutally maltreated insects I must particularly mention the anopheles mosquito. Ethel Douglas Hume (Mrs. Hedley Thomson), in her brilliant book *The Mindchangers*,[1] speaks wisely of the "crude fiction" which associates this charming little creature with malaria, and of the terrible campaigns which are being waged against it in Africa at the very moment when naturalists the world over are making propaganda for the preservation of big game there. It is simply a case of poor publicity: "Give a mosquito a bad name and hang him."

I hope I do not give the impression of being a crank; I am simply one who, by loving "all creatures great and small," adopts a consistent and logical attitude towards the animal kingdom. How can a man spare a lion yet kill an ant? How can he reject veal yet read books bound in calf? How can he oppose bull-fighting while continuing to wear leather shoes? Why, I even gave up wearing my plaited jute sandals when I discovered that animal glue had been used to attach the soles, and I have had the ivory keys of my piano replaced by plastic ones. It is only by waging relentless war against hypocrisy and brutality that we can hope to educate the people of the world to a better understanding of animals.

What is the attitude of the Christian Churches to all this? Father used to say that the villain of the piece (my phrase,

[1] Michael Joseph, 1939.

not his) was St. Thomas Aquinas, who introduced Aristote-
lian callousness into the teaching of Rome. "Thomism,
which is unfavourable to any recognition of rights in animals,
is the predominant philosophy among Roman Catholic
theologians,"[2] though it is not actually binding on the consciences of Roman Catholics.

John Wesley believed in the "heresy" of "a future life
for the brute creation" (wrote the Rev. Alexander Gor-
don); but Protestants and Roman Catholics alike deny a
soul to non-human animals. It is true that priests are quick
off the mark to bless children's pets; but then the Church—
and especially the Roman Church—is always ready to bless
anything, from rabbits to racing-cars, if it can thereby ex-
tend its influence or increase its popularity.

Of course St. Francis of Assisi, with his great reputation
as an animal lover, provides the Church with a very useful
precedent. But personally I feel that St. Francis made one
grave mistake: he preached *to* his birds; a better man
would have tried to learn *from* them. This anthropocentric
attitude has always tainted western thought.

So I still waver about the choice of a creed. For a time
I went to the Methodist chapel, but the services were not
to my liking. Nor was I sufficiently persuaded by St.
Francis to become a Clarisse. So perhaps I shall have to
become a Jain after all; but the trouble is that I do not
quite know how to set about it.

Father never much cared for, or attempted to understand,

[2] See Major C. W. Hume's brilliant book, *The Status of Animals in
the Christian Religion* (UFAW, 1957).

what he facetiously called my "leathered friends"; but sometimes he would half-absentmindedly pat a head or a rump as he walked down the garden to take the short cut to the Rectory. It was, as it happened, just such an innocent but ill-timed pat or two that cost him his life.

One afternoon as he was returning from the Rectory he came upon Tarquinia near the shrubbery. Now only the evening before we had been watching Shaw's *Androcles and the Lion* on telecolour (the one taste, besides reading, that we had in common), and it must suddenly have occurred to Father that he really ought to be able to do what a Roman slave could do. I do not mean that Tarquinia had a thorn in her paw; merely that Father thought that he should be able to establish friendly relations with her. So he went up to her and patted her on the back.

Tarquinia squealed.

Anyone who has had experience of otters will know that they always make their reactions perfectly clear. When they feel playful they hiss, whereas a squeal means anger; in other words, Tarquinia was *not* amused. But Father concluded that she was enjoying it, so he proceeded to chuck her once or twice under the chin and make himself (as he thought) agreeable to her. To Tarquinia, however, it seemed that she had given ample indication that she wanted to be left alone; since Father had failed to take the hint, he must take the consequences. So she turned on him and, with a single snap of her strong jaws, severed an artery in his right leg.

Lusty, the garden-boy, hearing Father cry out, ran to his assistance and at no small personal risk succeeded in

dragging Tarquinia off. I got Dr. Canning as soon as I
could, but unluckily he was on his rounds and there was a
considerable delay; meanwhile Father was bleeding like a pig,
and my fumbling efforts to make a tourniquet were almost
worse than useless. However, in the end he arrived—but
only to find that he had left his bag at Mrs. Eager's, five
miles away. I don't know just what went wrong: perhaps he left the tourniquet on too long. At all events,
gangrene set in and was further mismanaged, and a week
later Father died. All this occurred a few months before
my fiftieth birthday.

It so happened that, at the time of Father's death, I had only one other animal besides Tarquinia and my dogs and cat. This was a year-old cheetah called Chittagong ("Chit" for short), who had already caused me some trouble and embarrassment. Once he had disappeared for a whole week; but since he had never shown any inclination to attack a human being, I had felt there was no real need to inform the police. This proved a wise decision, because it must have been Chit who was responsible for the much reported "mystery" death of several cows and sheep, fortunately in a village about twelve miles from Disbourne; otherwise it might well have cost me a pretty penny. After Chit came back, I strengthened the bars of his cage. But I always looked upon him as one of my failures, because outside it I could never really trust him off a leash.

The second occasion on which Chit escaped was actually during Father's funeral service; he had managed to tear up a loose piece of his concrete floor and burrow his way out. This time he was missing for five days, and when he ultimately returned it was with one of Ralph Aylmer's clerical collars in his jaws. However there was no blood on it, so I felt I could safely assume that it had not been forcibly removed from its owner's neck. The next morning, at an hour when I knew that the Aylmers would be in church, I deposited the collar anonymously on their doorstep.

It was fortunate that Chit had a "den" in his enclosure into which he could withdraw when he needed shelter or solitude; thus no one in the house but myself was aware of his absences. It was assumed that he was "staying indoors," and of course I conscientiously took food there each day to keep up the deception. But less happily, on the second occasion Chit was seen, though only at some considerable distance, by several people. Yet luck was really still on my side—first because once again his misdeeds, other than the theft of the Rector's collar, had not been perpetrated in the immediate vicinity of Disbourne; and second, because the Press kindly decided that the miscreant, who had killed further cows and a foal, was a puma. There had been a previous puma scare in south-east England in the middle-sixties, and Surrey had remained "puma-conscious"; but for this particular misidentification I am eternally grateful to an office boy on the *Haslemere Gazette* who had once been on a choir outing to Whipsnade. Though hardly a soul in Disbourne could have told one big cat from another, it was well known that I had a cheetah and that there had never been any talk of a puma; and the Press, having once christened the marauder a puma, never reconsidered the matter.

However, events had forced me to realize that I could not continue to keep Chit, and I arranged for him to go to the Bristol Zoo, where he remains to this day. Chit was one of the few animals I have kept for whom I never really developed any deep affection, and I parted from him with no great sense of loss.

Father had died in the middle of April, and though Chit was safely installed in the Bristol Zoo by the second week in May, the puma continued to be "seen" in various parts of south-east England throughout the summer and autumn.

A kind of mass hysteria set in, and week after week the papers were full of stories of "the Surrey Puma." A housewife in Abinger Hammer found it feeding out of her dustbin. Two Boy Scouts of unblemished reputation reported that they had fed it with dog-biscuits in a wood near Beare Green and were awarded the Baden Powell Medal (second class) for valour. A clergyman near Leatherhead surprised it in his vestry and took a photograph of it which unfortunately did not come out. In Blitworth, where a cow had died of old age, the puma was held responsible; in spite of Press assurances that pumas never attacked man, something very near to panic seized the whole village, whose children were escorted to and from school by volunteers with rifles and shotguns. The puma was seen almost simultaneously on the afternoon of July 9th in Elstead, Bucks Green, Godstone, Holmbury St. Mary and Ripley—places many miles apart, and there was hardly a village in Surrey or north Sussex without its tale of spoors or midnight wailings.

The local papers had all given an accurate account (taken from the *Encyclopaedia Britannica,* 11th Edition) of the physical characteristics of a puma, which is not in the least like a cheetah; so it was hardly surprising, I suppose, that everyone who saw—or alleged that they had seen—the beast reported an animal exactly answering to this description. Plaster casts of spoors were taken and submitted to the Natural History Museum, but they always proved to be those of a fox or a badger, or to be too blurred for purposes of identification. By October the Press had decided that the Surrey puma was no longer "news."

Reports continued to pour in; but the men (and particularly the women) of Surrey, finding that their letters were no longer published, gradually abandoned the hope of seeing their names in print in this context and turned their attention to more rewarding topics.

The puma was, it was generally agreed, dead—or at all events done for.

"Of course you will have Tarquinia put to sleep," said Helen Aylmer after Father's funeral. She is always a little too ready to run other people's lives for them.

I must confess that the idea had never crossed my mind. Getting rid of Tarquinia, either by having her put down or by presenting her to a zoo, would not bring Father back, even if such a thing were desirable. And I was passionately attached to her.

"I think it would cause a lot of talk in the village if you didn't," Helen added.

All my life this "village" threat had been used by Father to thwart my plans: "I don't know what *the village* will think of your shorts"; "I think *the village* will be rather surprised if you don't attend," and so on. What on earth had it to do with *the village* whether or not I kept Tarquinia? Yet I knew that in a small community one could not wholly flout public opinion. I said I would think it over; and in the end—very weakly, I know—I offered her to Whipsnade, where at least I would be able to see her from time to time.

I forget whether or not I have mentioned that Tarquinia was a Japanese otter (*Lutra whiteleyi*)—something of a rarity, and Whipsnade accepted her with alacrity. I drove her there and handed her over to one of the keepers—a man whose name, curiously enough, was Whiteley. I could see at once that Tarquinia took to him, and this was a shred of comfort. But it was also plain that she understood exactly what was happening to her—and possibly even the reason for her banishment; as I was about to leave, she broke away from Whiteley and came whimpering to throw herself into my arms. It was heart-rending.

For a time I continued to visit her, but her affectionate welcome when I arrived, and her abject misery on my leaving, soon became more than I could bear, and in the end I stopped going; since I could not have her, it was better to try to forget her. It was this double loss, almost simultaneously, of Tarquinia and (the admittedly less-loved) Chit which seemed such a cruel blow on the part of Fate. Treble loss really, if one includes Father.

When I was a child I had a book of songs, one of which was about a poodle. It began, if I recollect rightly:

> *Once there lived a little poodle*
> *And his coat was white as snow,*
> *And his master loved him dearly*
> *And his mistress loved him so . . .*

I cannot recall the middle stanzas, which described the poodle's death (of apoplexy resulting from over-feeding) and his mistress's vow never again to expose herself to such misery by the acquisition of another. The poem ended:

> *But how weak is human nature,*
> *For ere three weeks had passed*
> *She had bought* another *poodle-dog*
> *Exactly like the last!*

I felt much the same about Tarquinia, but I held out for a great deal longer than three weeks. All through the summer I moped about the house and garden, where everything reminded me of her. I took no pleasure in my dogs and could hardly bring myself to exercise them. In the end I put away her toys (which Whipsnade had rejected), emptied the pool where we had so often played together, and tried to forget her. The trouble is that once you have kept an otter, nothing else will take its place; but *the village,* which could not tell one otter from another, would, if I bought a new one, merely think that I had changed my mind and callously fetched Tarquinia back.

One day while I was browsing in Smith's bookshop in Haslemere I chanced upon, and bought, a little volume entitled *How to be a Widow of Fifty,* written, it was stated, "by the author of *How to be a Widow of Seventy."* Though I did not actually qualify, I felt that the situation in which I now found myself was comparable. The book proved to be facetious in style and depressing in substance:

At first [wrote the author] you will doubtless find yourself still invited from time to time to the houses where you and your husband were formerly welcome. But these invitations, which you must realise are only made *out of pity,* will soon cease. You will be dropped. It is now that you must set about making a life of your own. Say to yourself every morning as you dress, "I am NOT YET OLD. There is still MUCH THAT I CAN DO." If, as is probable, you lack the talent to occupy yourself with any intellectual or artistic pursuit, you will have to fall back on gardening and good works. Interest yourself in the Women's Institute. Join the church choir, where keenness will probably be considered a perfectly adequate substitute for musicianship or a voice. Guide the Girl Guides. Organize nature rambles for the Boy Scouts. Sew socks for the Sudanese or make mufflers for the Mexicans —it matters little which. Try to grow taller tulips or beastlier begonias than your neighbour. ALWAYS KEEP YOUR CHIN UP. And above all, KEEP A PET . . .

This "being dropped" did not worry me in the least, for we had rarely dined out anywhere except at the Rectory. As to gardening and good works, I despised the former (which is a mug's game) and was morally certain that I had little aptitude for the latter. I can neither knit nor sew, and Girl Guides bore me. As for boys, I am only interested in delinquents—and Boy Scouts are, by definition, already (in theory at any rate) saved. My chin is by nature so recessive as to be quite unsuited to "upping." There was no nearby Borstal at which I might have worked, but I thought that the salvation of Lusty, my delinquent garden-boy, might perhaps count as social work. I admit that I am fond of *good* music—*too* fond of it, in fact, to subject

myself twice weekly to Hymns A. and M. As to the PET
—well, that, of course, was the *real* answer to it all: I *must*
find another animal to love.

I have not, I think, as yet made it clear that as a family
we were almost extinct. The only relation I now had in
the whole world was an uncle in Canada—a brother of
Father's. He was a very rich mining engineer, and as he
had quarrelled with Father fifty or more years ago I had
never even met him; but after Father's death he had written
me a nice letter offering to help me if I was short of money.
None the less, I now felt very alone in the world. True I
had not found Father *simpatico;* but at least he had been
company of a kind, and in a way I missed him. At night,
especially, the house seemed depressingly empty, for since
I no longer really had need of full-time help I had parted
with "our faithful Martha." In her place, three mornings a
week, a Mrs. Dudge came up from the village to "do" for
me; and though I cannot pretend that she was intellectually
stimulating, I came to look forward to her "days" and her
ceaseless flow of village gossip. She was a plump, homely
old soul—a bit of a boozer but an excellent worker. In the
evening I watched telecolour, which at least distracted my
thoughts and was a kind of company.

Thus drearily the summer passed until a day came
round which could, I suppose, be considered a kind of a
landmark in my life: my fiftieth birthday. Little did I
guess what it had in store for me.

2

As everybody knows, there is a firm called Interflora which is prepared, for a trifling sum, to deliver a bunch of seasonable flowers to mark the birthday or some other anniversary of a distant friend. The corresponding and more recently instituted service of Interfauna is, however, not so widely publicized as it deserves to be.

It functions in exactly the same manner as Interflora, though it is a good deal more expensive. Naturally the choice of animal is left to the discretion of the firm, which selects from its stock something that it considers appropriate and which approximates in value the sum of money available. If this represents a mere token gift—say a pound or two—the recipient may be offered a pair of budgerigars or a hamster. For ten or twenty pounds he might get a pedigree puppy or a rather shop-soiled monkey. And should it be a matter of a hundred pounds or more, then a van might deliver an opossum or a small zebra at the door of the astonished householder. It is, of course, the element of surprise that is believed to constitute so large a part of the pleasure of the recipient. But it may not be so easy for a Londoner who finds himself, suddenly and unforewarned, the possessor of an animal with crazy house-habits and exacting dietary requirements. While nobody has ever been known to refuse roses, I believe there have been quite a number of cases where handsome and valuable animals—camels and so forth —have been rejected outright. (Even accepted gifts have been known to outlive their infantile charm; I have read that in New York no longer wanted alligators, flushed in despair down the W.C., have thriven and indeed bred in the city's sewers). Interfauna cannot be an easy service to run.

At three o'clock on the afternoon of my birthday a private delivery van deposited on my doorstep a small slatted crate obviously containing a live animal. From its size, and the very imperfect view that I had of it through the slats, I thought it might be a Siamese cat, or possibly some kind of a rodent such as a musquash or a marmot. It spat at me with surprising accuracy through a chink in the crate.

The driver of the van had his arm in a sling and some ugly scratches on his cheek. "Omar's got a nasty temper, Ma'am," he said, pointing at the crate. "I'd watch out if I was you." Having lived with animals all my life, I saw no reason why I should receive advice of this nature from a car-driver, a mere mechanic; a coachman might have been different. My first impulse was to tell the man that animals only attacked those who did not know how to handle them; but I refrained. In view of what subsequently occurred, I am glad that I remained silent.

Attached to the lid of the crate was an envelope inscribed:

IMPORTANT
READ CAREFULLY BEFORE OPENING THE CRATE

I curbed my impatience and obeyed the injunction. The enclosure, which had been completed by hand, read as follows:

INTERFAUNA EXPRESS DELIVERY SERVICE

THIS young male bandersnatch IS A PRESENT FROM Robert Bavistock TO his niece Rose ON THE OCCASION OF her fiftieth BIRTHDAY. His NAME IS Omar AND he IS about eighteen months old. HAPPY BIRTHDAY TO YOU! FOR FULL INSTRUCTIONS SEE ATTACHED LEAFLET.

I suddenly recollected that I had told my uncle, when I wrote to him after Father's death, that I was fond of animals and that I was going to have to send Tarquinia away. He had asked my age, and I suppose I must have said that I would be fifty on August 17th. But how nice it was of him to have remembered and to have gone to all that trouble!

The leaflet said:

The Bandersnatch (*Persohyrax frumiosus*) is a native of Hyrcania, the new Russo-Persian Republic on the shores of the Caspian. A denizen of the Elburz mountains, it is accustomed to withstand moderately low temperatures and in the south of England may safely be kept all the year round in a garden enclosure provided with stout meshing. It is by nature a friendly creature, though sometimes frumious at first with strangers; thick gloves are therefore advisable when handling it in the early stages. In time, however, it will become completely tame and even affectionate, and may then, if preferred, be safely introduced into the living-room . . .

There followed full details of feeding and general management, and the recommendation to consult a veterinary surgeon *at once* in the event of any difficulty. In smaller print towards the end, I read, "When irritated or frustrated, the Bandersnatch may, like the Skunk, sometimes emit a slight odour. This is merely a dumb animal's way of registering anxiety or disapproval, and it should *never* be scolded for it." The notice then reverted to block capitals and closed:

LOVE YOUR BANDERSNATCH
AND YOUR BANDERSNATCH WILL LOVE YOU
YOU ARE ABOUT TO BEGIN A WONDERFUL FRIENDSHIP

Meanwhile the man was growing impatient.

"If you want that hell-cat carried anywhere," he said, "let's get on with it. I've got two hyenas in the van, and a wolf-cub, and they don't like being kept waiting."

I found his manner offensive; but the crate was too heavy to manhandle alone, and Lusty was not there to help. So together we carried it round into the garden and down to the large wire-netted enclosure which until recently had housed my beloved Tarquinia. As we walked I offered the man some advice. If he did not care for animals, might he not be wise to look for some other job? He did not choose to answer, so I thought it would be good to give him a practical demonstration. When we reached the cage I said, "Gloves are really quite unnecessary. I am now going to open the crate."

With an agility of which I would have doubted him capable, the man skipped out of the cage and slammed the door. I withdrew the bolts of the crate, unlocked the padlock with the key provided, and lifted the lid.

Were you or I to be shut up for hours in a very small trunk, we would doubtless emerge from it with acute cramp and be incapable of movement for some seconds at least. But no sooner had I opened the lid than Omar shot out with the momentum of a jack-in-the-box and began to roar round the enclosure like one possessed. Finally he stopped dead in the farthest corner and faced me. He seemed to be summing me up, and I had the uncomfortable feeling that I was getting very low marks.

I must admit that at first sight Omar was not particularly glamorous or prepossessing. He had none of the sensuous

elegance of the cat tribe, none of the "cuddly" charm of the great panda and the bears. He lacked the wide-eyed beauty of the bush-baby, the delightful absurdity and striking coloration of many of the monkeys. In the small mammal house at the Zoo, every visitor pauses to admire the red acouchi, the blotched genet and the red-footed ground squirrel; but were there a bandersnatch (which at that time there was not, as I later learned), I think the world would probably pass him by. He has no particular feature to arrest the attention. Omar looked, in fact, like a rather plump, frumpish little German *Hausfrau* in a too-tight-fitting bargain-basement fur coat.

He was about the size of a rabbit, and I presumed him to be a rodent related perhaps to the guinea-pig or the marmot. His coat was nut-brown, darkening to mahogany on the underparts; but on his back and nearer to the tail than the head, was a crisp tuft of white hair which reminded me of the white forelock of the painter Whistler. His eyes were prune-coloured and beady; his muzzle, which was hairless, might have been made from the leather of a very old club armchair. But from his upper lip there sprouted perhaps a dozen wiry black bristles, like the horsehairs that emerge from those same armchairs when the leather finally falls apart. Other similar bristles or guard-hairs grew at random elsewhere on his body, projecting six inches or more from the soft fur. The feet seemed to have three or four toes, and the tail was small and inconspicuous.

This much I took in while Omar was doing his circus turn. But when he came to a halt and confronted me, I knew from the look on his face that I was in for trouble. I had not long to wait. Almost before I was aware that he had charged, I felt his sharp teeth deep in my calf; and when, instinctively, I put my hand down to try to disengage his jaws, he turned his head and bit my thumb. Then, as though to indicate that the first lesson was at an end, he moved away and took no further notice of me.

The bites were painful (though one gets a curious masochistic pleasure from being bitten by an animal); but far more wounding was the coarse laughter of the van-man.

"It's nothing," I said when I had made my escape from the cage. "He was only playing."

"Rather with you than with me, Ma'am," said the van-man rudely. But blood was pouring from my hand and leg, and it was not so easy to laugh it off. The man offered to fetch bandages and antiseptic from his van, but I told him not to trouble. I still had my pride.

Naturally one of my first concerns was to find out all I could about bandersnatches.

Now I am bound to confess that I had never realized that there actually was such an animal as a bandersnatch: I thought it was a fictitious creature invented by Lewis Carroll. But the *Encyclopaedia Britannica* confirmed that the bandersnatch did exist, though it added that it was only very rarely to be seen in captivity. The article gave the usual incomprehensible information about cheek-dentition, dorsal vertebrae, and so on. It said that in the bandersnatch the alisphenoid canal was present, but the bullae surprisingly small—and so on, at considerable length. It concluded: "In its habits, many of which are very engaging, this ferocious but basically lovable animal may be compared to its relative the tree-hyrax, *Dendrohyrax dorsalis,* a native of the forests of central and southern Africa; it is not, however, nocturnal, and though a skilful climber it lives in warrens and not in the tree-tops.

By far the most surprising thing I learned was that the bandersnatch was not a rodent, but an ungulate—zoologically to be placed somewhere between the rhinoceros or elephant and the horse. Like the true hyraxes, it be-

longs to the Procaviidae—a small and somewhat per-
plexing sub-order of ungulates whose members are dwarfed
by most of their near relatives. Later, when I was able to
examine Omar's feet, I found that his toes terminated in
little black nails, so that the paw looked not unlike the
hand of a tiny Negro baby.

I turned to Lewis Carroll. You will doubtless remember
that Carroll exhorted his son (or more probably, since he
was a bachelor in Holy Orders, someone else's son) to
"shun the frumious Bandersnatch." "Frumious" means, of
course, "ill-tempered," "savage," "fierce." I would be the
first to admit that Omar was not, at the start, co-operative,
and there were times when, like Carroll's Banker, I would
gladly have

> . . . offered a cheque
> (Drawn "to bearer") for seven-pounds-ten

could I thereby have been guaranteed immunity from attack. For a whole week, each time I entered his enclosure
he flew at me. Father's old cricket-pads to some extent
protected my shins, but his batting-gloves were not really
effective; leather would (I must in all honesty admit) have
been more tooth-proof. Any attempt to examine Omar's
alisphenoid canal, check his dentition, or discover whether
or not I would be surprised by the smallness of his bullae,
would at this stage have been tantamount to suicide.

But I blame myself entirely for these setbacks. Once the
barrier between man and "beast" (odious word!) has been
broken down, it is only very rarely that the most cordial

relationship is not established; and if there is a delay in the establishment of this relationship, then it must almost always be man's fault. I was soon to find in Omar the most devoted of companions.

Another point. It can hardly have escaped the notice of even the most casual reader of Lewis Carroll's poem that he urged the lad to "shun" the bandersnatch simply because the word "shun" happened to rhyme with "son." Had the poem been addressed to a daughter, then very likely he would have recommended that she

> . . . *bought a*
> Bewitching Bandersnatch

or some such. In short, we are forced to the conclusion that Carroll knew little and cared less about bandersnatches. Probably he had never even seen one except behind the bars of a zoo, where as likely as not it was troating at children who had been teasing it. Certainly he can never have kept and trained one himself, or he would not have written such arrant nonsense. The bandersnatch, as I hope to show, is the most intelligent of the so-called "dumb" animals; its intellect is in many ways far superior to man's. We may dismiss Carroll's account as ignorant or prejudiced, and in either case worthless.

After enduring a week of unremitting hostility I decided that I would adopt a new technique: I would give Omar the clearest possible evidence that I was not afraid of him, that I had no intention of being intimidated, and that the sooner he realized it the better. So I abandoned Father's shin-pads and gloves, and the following morning, feeling very like a Christian on his way to the lions, walked un-armed into his enclosure.

I braced myself to receive the attack. After all, I told myself, he will only savage me; he is very unlikely to kill me. But I must confess that I was nervous, though I did my best to conceal the fact. To my astonishment Omar did not rush at me, but stood stock still in the far corner of the cage. Then he fixed me with a kind of enquiring, penetrating stare such as a connoisseur might give to a dubious Rembrandt. Finally he came slowly towards me in the most amiable way, dittering gently, and rubbed his body against my bandaged leg. I understood this to mean that he wanted me to pick him up, and rather fearfully I did so. He lay quite still in my bandaged arms, and then licked my lacerated cheek.

From that moment, in fact, the "beautiful friendship" predicted by Interfauna had begun. I was truly amazed. Normally the winning of the confidence of an animal is a gradual process requiring great patience and often inter-rupted by setbacks due to misunderstandings; but with Omar it was just as though he had *reasoned* his way to this change of attitude. It was as though he had said to him-self, "I've given her a week of *Blitzkrieg* and it hasn't had the slightest effect. All right: she's won. Now let's forget about it and try a different treatment." The time had ob-viously come for me to take him back with me to the house. I carried him across the lawn and into the drawing-room.

When I put Omar down on the floor, he stretched him-

self once or twice, yawned, and then set out to inspect
the room. In fact he behaved rather like a visitor going
round a "stately home" under the care of the National
Trust, though he took liberties of a kind that the Trust
would not have welcomed. First he examined the two large
watercolours of Venice and other Victorian bric-à-brac
which had come to us from my grandmother (Mother's
mother); we had always meant to clear it all away, but
somehow or other it had never got done. Next he seated
himself on the sofa, bouncing up and down several times
to test its resilience. He surveyed the chairs, and seemed
especially interested in a rather nice Caucasian rug of
mine. Then he sniffed at a bowl of dahlias which Mrs.
Dudge had brought up from the village (for personally I
never bother about flowers—indeed I consider it cruel to
pick them). Finally he jumped on to the piano and, to my
intense astonishment, shot straight up the wall till he reached
the cornice, which is about thirteen feet high; then he de-
scended by way of a Medici print of Titian's "Sacred and
Profane Love" as far as the mantel-piece. Here he paused
a minute or two, a contented smile on his face; he might
have been saying, "All right. This room suits me. I'll take
it."

So that was that. I soon fixed up baskets for him in
several of the rooms, and in the corner of the drawing-
room, hidden behind a little pair of red velvet curtains, a
tray covered with sand for his lavatory; animals are grateful for this privacy. Fortunately it was not one of Mrs.
Dudge's mornings, for I preferred to present her with the
fait accompli.

Next morning, before I had had time to warn her about our new house-guest, Mrs. Dudge entered the kitchen to find Omar sitting in a soup-plate on the cooler end of the kitchen range. It was a bad start.

I was sorry, because in every other respect Omar soon settled down so happily in the house. But between him and Mrs. Dudge there developed an antipathy which increased from day to day. Having learned that he came from Hyrcania, which I explained was in Asia, she always referred to him as "that heathen animal." I could not help the feeling that she was being very unwise in antagonizing him by little incivilities such as deliberately shutting the door in his face just as he was about to go through it, and so on; Omar could be a good friend, but I was equally sure that he could be a dangerous enemy.

One of the first things that I set out to study was Omar's technique for moving from place to place. For travelling horizontally, he had three distinct gaits with nothing intermediate. The first was was an enormously dignified slow walk which always reminded me of high-ranking clergy processing up a cathedral aisle; its speed must have been well under one mile an hour. The second was a brisk, businesslike trot with little paws twinkling; it meant that Omar had a definite and moderately urgent objective, and it carried him along at the speed of a man's unhurried running. But more remarkable was his top-gear performance, which was reserved for a real emergency. Omar then seemed to shoot through the air as though propelled from the barrel of a gun. I cannot begin to guess the speed in miles per hour; but I once photographed him thus, using an exposure of a five-hundredth of a second, and the result was simply a blur. Put in musical terms, these three *tempi* might be described as *largo, allegretto,* and *presto prestissimo* respectively. Occasionally he would stand for a moment on his hind legs, but he always moved on all fours.

But even more astonishing was his achievement in a vertical plane. "The feet of the bandersnatch," I read, "have special naked pads for traction; these pads are kept continually moist by glandular secretion and have a muscle arrangement that retracts the middle of the sole. This forms a hollow, which is a suction cap of considerable clinging power." So long as Omar was in his wired enclosure he could not make use of this remarkable gadget; but in the house he made no distinction between the horizontal and

the vertical when he felt in need of exercise. Indeed I sometimes wondered whether he might not be able to cross a
ceiling if the need arose; but I never saw him attempt it.

I had presumed that there would be the problem of
keeping Omar amused, but I was quite wrong: he was
perfectly happy amusing himself. Tarquinia had been a child
who had to be perpetually entertained. If you gave her a
ball she would play with it like a kitten, or lie on her
back and let it roll gently down her plump little body. But
within two minutes she had tired of this game and was
nuzzling my face and caressing me and demanding a new
toy. It was all very charming; but it was also very exhaust-
ing and very time-consuming.

When I gave the same ball to Omar he first sniffed at it
and (I suppose) registered its otter scents. Then he examined it as if he were adjudicating a prize melon at a
horticultural show. It had the word BUNJIBAL written on it,
and he now turned the ball slowly round exactly as if he
were reading it letter by letter. Next he pushed it a foot
or so from him and gazed at it thoughtfully; I was almost
going to say that he studied it *scientifically,* as though he
were making a rough estimate of the value of π or wondering what the formula was for the volume of a sphere.
Finally he picked it up, carried it to the wastepaper basket
and dropped it in. He had told me, as clearly as if he had
spoken, that he had no further use for this infant's bauble.

He was amazingly mature; in fact I often had the feeling
—the rather uncomfortable feeling—that he was much more
intelligent, and infinitely older, than myself. Though he
would sometimes sit and stare for an hour or more on

end, it was never a *vacant* stare. His expression changed from minute to minute, as though registering the development of a definite train of thought. He would listen at-

tentively to almost anything serious on the gramophone or the wireless; but once, when I had something rather cheap on the Light Programme, he rose and *turned it off!* He liked classical music, especially Beethoven and Mozart, but Wagner drove him out of the room. However I think his favourite composer was Richard Strauss, and perhaps *Till Eulenspiegel,* of which I had a record, the work which most excited him. In the evening he would often sit on my lap and watch telecolour, his eyes glued to the screen just as though he were taking in everything that was happening. He enjoyed nature and wild life films, travelogues, and the ballet; but he by no means despised a good thriller.

I discovered, quite early on in my relationship with Omar, that he preferred it to remain strictly platonic. Most animals, once they have accepted man, like to be stroked, tickled, patted, petted and made much fuss of; but Omar remained cold, aloof, dignified. Though he sometimes, as I have said, consented to sit on my lap, he made it clear that he considered it as nothing more than a chair of convenient height, perhaps more comfortably upholstered than the genuine article. When I felt in the mood to caress an animal I generally had to turn to my dogs and my cat.

This reminds me that so far I have made only the briefest reference to my other pets at this time. Of the cat—a homely old body much preoccupied with the pursuit of her own comfort, very self-indulgent, and very jealous of Omar who ignores her—there is really not much to say. Her name is Tally, this being short for "Italian"; I called her this because she reminded me of one of those well-fed, black, spherical, glossy (yet dusty) little priests one sees everywhere in Italy. Most of her time is spent in the kitchen, as near as possible to the stove. Mrs. Dudge tolerates her, but no more.

My two alsatians, Shilling and Penny, are a joy to me. I know they are sometimes a bit boisterous with strangers, and that they *did* scratch up a plant or two—what Helen Aylmer ludicrously described as "fifty pounds' worth of damage"—in the Rectory garden. But that snarling and growling and jumping up are simply signs of high spirits, and when they bite it is only from fear, never in anger. People are so silly and touchy about this kind of thing. For example the postman, who has only been bitten twice, will no longer bring letters up to the house but insists upon leaving them in a box at the end of the drive; and when I complained, he said that *he* would complain to the police if I did not accept this arrangement. Of course it is he who

is really the loser—when the Christmas-box season comes
round; I can see no possible reason why, in the Welfare
State, I should squander my money to subsidize cowardice.

It has been fascinating watching Omar with Shilling and
Penny. On his very first day in the house he gave a little
demonstration of frightfulness, but thereafter a *modus
vivendi* was established. Omar treats them much as a senior
partner in a firm might treat a couple of well-meaning but
rather stupid junior clerks. He looks pityingly at them
when they lie asleep on the hearthrug during a particularly
absorbing telecolour programme. And they, for their part,
seem to recognize that he belongs to a superior world in
which they have no real part.

After Omar had been living with me for about a fortnight, I began to try to analyse the various sounds that
he uttered.

First there were certain general sounds which seemed to
indicate a state of mind. A gentle dittering implied con-
tentedness or approval, a sustained trooling, on a note about
a third below middle C, unhappiness or disapproval.
Chuffing meant impatience. Troating signified anger, and
was a warning to anyone present to take cover. But there
were also a number of sounds which conveyed a more
precise need or intention; these I soon came to understand,
and I will try to describe some of them:

"Kkgk . . . rrr": "I am about to bite."

"Kkgk . . . rrrrrrr": "I am about to bite hard."

"Oh"—said in a very "refined" voice: "I want my water-
bowl refilling."

"Peeee": "I am going to the lavatory."

"Peee-peee-peee . . ." (like the "put your money in now" signal on a public telephone): "I want to go to the lavatory, but you have forgotten to bring back the tray after you emptied it."

"Oomph-pa": "Something is hurting me."

"Tfn": "I want my dinner."

"Oi!": "Come here!"

"NININIM!": "There is an emergency."

There were also certain exclamations—"wow!" (surprise or joy), "ugh!" (disgust), "ooch!" (sudden pain), and so on—which were used much as we ourselves use them. In fact, I could not help noticing how human were many of Omar's utterances. "Peee" and "oi!" were self-explanatory; "oh," as he pronounced it, sounded very like the "French "eau"; "tfn" might well be "tiffin"; "nīnīnīn" could only be "999"; and readers of Barry Pain's *Eliza* will remember that "oomph-pa" was the cry of anguish reiterated by the parlour-maid with the slipped knee-cap. All this was surely more than a coincidence. Or was it?

It took me a little longer to discover that Omar could also imitate to perfection a variety of natural and other sounds. One day I put the kettle on the kitchen stove and then came back to the drawing-room to wait till it boiled. I had filled it with cold water; yet barely a minute later I could have sworn that I heard it boiling. When I reached the kitchen I found the kettle still almost cold, and Omar warming his front paws on the stove, his face wearing something very like a grin. Yet it was not until this practical joke had been played on me several times that I understood. Omar obviously realized that I had understood; the joke had now lost its point, and he did not repeat it.

One day the Aylmers were having tea with me and suddenly, in a pause in the conversation, Helen seemed to utter an abdominal rumble of quite unusual richness and volume.

Ralph said, *"Really,* Helen!"

"It *wasn't* me, Ralph!"

"It certainly wasn't me," I said.

The Aylmers looked puzzled; and I was puzzled too—until I saw Omar slip guiltily out from under Helen's chair and creep back to his basket. He did not care for Helen.

Another game of Omar's was to imitate the mewing of Tally wanting to be let in; of this he never tired, and in the end it really became rather a nuisance. Yet another—and this was still more annoying—was his habit of altering the hands of the grandfather clock. Omar was certainly a tease.

But something yet stranger was soon to happen. One evening we were listening to a telecolour talk by Professor Tanker on the origins of the First World War. Omar was sitting on my knees, his little grape-coloured eyes glued to the screen; quite exceptionally, he had allowed me to take his front paws between my hands. Professor Tanker had already propounded more than one rather far-fetched theory, and I had noticed that Omar was becoming restless. "Sit still!" I said, gently stroking him. "I want to listen." At this moment the Professor remarked that the *real* cause of the outbreak of war in 1914 was the acute shortage of matchboxes in Herzogovina. Omar immediately rose in my lap, arched his back, spat, and then said, perfectly distinctly, "Bilge!"

Alice, when the White Rabbit suddenly said, "Oh dear! Oh dear! I shall be too late," did not at first "think it so *very* much out of the way" that an animal should have spoken. I too, for a moment, took it as perfectly natural that Omar should have used this way of making known his opinion—an opinion which, in fact, exactly coincided with my own; I was more occupied in my mind with the

question as to whether thought-transference, in which I firmly believe, was involved. Then gradually I became aware of the oddness of the situation. Or was it after all *I,* not Omar, who had spoken?

"What did you say?" I asked.

"Piffle!" said Omar. Then he jumped off my lap, stretched himself, yawned a couple of times, and retired to his basket.

Part II
VIDIT

I

Cet animal est très méchant;
Quand on l'attaque, il se défend.

Next morning while I was dressing I reflected upon the extraordinary events of the night before. Had Omar merely said "bilge!", I would have been prepared to write it off as no more than a coincidentally apposite belch; after all, "belch" is onomatopoeic, and very similar to "bilge" in sound. But how to account for the "piffle" that followed?

There was nothing that I could do for the moment other than await events. If he had really spoken, then surely he would speak again. I began to watch him still more closely.

I had made inquiries from Interfauna as to Omar's provenance. He had not, I learned, been bred in captivity, but had been taken in the Elburz as a cub and flown to London from Tehran. But his previous owner—the man, I gathered, who had caught him and brought him to England—was now back in the East and did not wish his name to be disclosed.

It is of course well known that all animals dislike draughts; but Omar, in view of his alfresco childhood, seemed to me to be curiously hypersensitive on this point. Father used to call me "a fresh air fiend," and I admit that I like to have doors and windows open, even in mid-winter; it was often a subject of dispute between us. Omar did not (as did Father) mind the cold, but he shared his dislike of draughts; he could not himself shut the heavy sash-windows, but he would often push the french window to with his front paws.

Now one morning, when I had left the french window open, Omar rose grumpily from his snug basket, *allegretto*'d across the room, and shut it with a bang. It so happened that I was at the moment completely absorbed in an article in *Country Life* on "Traditional Designs in Bird Baths in the Isle of Man," but subconsciously I absorbed what was happening and registered his irritation; then the affairs of Omar passed out of my mind, and without any intention of hurting his feelings I got up and re-opened the french window.

Suddenly a voice said, "Shut that bloody door!"

Father often used to say, "Rose, *do* shut that door!" and my immediate reaction was that it was quite out of charac-ter for him to use the word "bloody." I got up and shut it; only then did I realize that it was Omar who had spoken.

I had of course already heard Omar say (or *seem* to say) "bilge!" and "piffle!"; but on thinking the matter over I could not *absolutely* persuade myself that he had really spoken those two apposite English words. Was it not more likely that I had put an appropriate interpretation upon what had actually been a belch followed by a hiccup? But this time there could surely be no doubt whatever: Omar had said, with absolute clarity, with no possibility of ambiguity, "Shut that bloody door!"

The effect on me was so bewildering that for a moment I felt quite faint. Though I am not in the habit of drinking whisky at eleven o'clock in the morning, I went through to the larder to fetch a bottle that I remembered having put there. In the kitchen I came upon Mrs. Dudge.

"Good gracious, Miss, are you all right? You look as if you'd seen a ghost."

"I'm all right. I've had a bit of a shock, but I'm all right really. I'm going to take a strong whisky."

It was foolish of me to have used the word "shock," for Mrs. Dudge would not leave it alone. What *kind* of a shock? and so on, *ad nauseam*. "Just a slight shock," I said. "Only something rather odd that happened. It really was nothing; I feel better already."

Indeed I did. I dislike the taste of whisky, but I had more than once had experience of its efficacy in a crisis. I was soon sufficiently myself again to observe that since Mrs. Dudge's arrival the level of the whisky in the bottle had dropped several inches, and to make a mental note to keep it locked up in the future. I also found myself wondering what kind of a legend Mrs. Dudge would spread around the village.

When I got back to the drawing-room I found Omar apparently sound asleep in his basket, a seraphic smile on his face. I knew that I must have it out with him; so I woke him, picked him up and, seating myself on the sofa, took him on my knee.

"Now, Omar," I said. *"What did you say?* You said— and you know you did—'Shut that bloody door.' Didn't you? DIDN'T YOU?"

So absolute was the blankness that came over Omar's face, that I immediately began to doubt again. Perhaps I was ill. Perhaps I ought to see a doctor. One often heard of people "seeing things"; probably there were also people who "heard things." The second whisky had been a mistake: I now felt rather tight and totally bemused. I went to bed, missed lunch, and slept till dinner-time. Next morning I went to see Dr. Canning.

Bruce Canning is one of those amiable practitioners who combine the manner of a Harley Street specialist with the knowledge of a backward first-year medical student. So long as you are with him you are hypnotized, as it were, into accepting his omniscience; once away from him, you doubt whether he knows, within a yard or two, where the kidneys are located. To put it crudely, he had probably as good as murdered Father; yet such was the force of habit that I had not broken away from him. Also he was the only doctor in Disbourne.

I told him exactly what had occurred, keeping nothing back; he looked wisdom itself and said that my case was far from unique. Then I was thumped and sounded. My reflexes were tested, my pulse and temperature taken. Many questions were asked (for no one could deny his thoroughness), and I was as usual reprimanded for being a vegetarian. Finally he said:

"My dear Miss Bavistock, you are suffering from delayed shock after the death of your father. Parrots, as you very well know, talk; but there is no animal that talks *rationally*. These are hallucinations, and the best thing you can do is to take a long cruise. Or what about your uncle in Canada? You have one, I believe. Why not go and spend the autumn —or should I say the fall?—with him. You would see beavers and other interesting animals—perhaps even a grizzly bear or two. And you would come back a different woman."

I thanked him. But I hadn't the slightest intention of taking his advice.

Orthodox medicine having failed, I decided to try an unorthodox practitioner in Ealing who had cured Helen Aylmer of varicose veins by infusions of Peruvian liverwort. I did not mention to him how I had heard of him, nor did I disclose my name or address; but having taken these precautions, I had no anxiety about giving him full details of my trouble. He listened without any great show of interest and then said:

"I can cure you. But first I shall need some parings from the finger-nails of your right hand. These I shall send for analysis to a colleague of mine in Bermuda; return in a month's time and I will tell you what he says. Meanwhile this"—and he produced a small phial of purple glass— "will relieve the tension. This wonder-drug is widely used by the Chunchos Indians of Eastern Peru and is derived from a local species of Hepatica, or liverwort. Kindly pay my secretary as you leave, and give her your name and address."

I deposited six guineas and a fictitious name and address on her desk.

"Good morning, Miss Arbuthnot. Dr. Leberkraut will be keeping in touch."

I doubted it. However, having purchased Peruvian liverwort at the rate of about two shillings a drop, I thought I might as well try it. After two days of the treatment—though whether *post* or *propter* I cannot pretend to say—I was completely cured. In other words, all uncertainty had vanished. I was *not* suffering from hallucinations. I was *not* ill. Beyond all shadow of doubt, Omar had ordered me to "shut that bloody door."

Dr. Leberkraut (or his Bermudan colleague) is still in possession of my nail-parings, and he is very welcome to keep them.

I must now mention an episode that made no sense at the time but which I was to understand later on. Or rather, that the sense it *appeared* to make at the time was later shown to be nonsense.

I had provided a basket for Omar at the foot of my bed, but he had made it plain that he preferred to sleep in his day-basket in the drawing-room; I therefore let him have his own way. One night I could not sleep, so I got out of bed to find a sleeping-pill. I then noticed a light shining across the lawn; it was coming from the study, which opened out of the drawing-room and was immediately beneath my bedroom. I put on a dressing-gown and, taking the stout stick which I always keep near my bed, crept silently downstairs to investigate. But when I reached the hall I could see that there was no chink of light under the library door. I opened it, went in and turned on the light; there was no one, and the windows were bolted. In the drawing-room Omar lay curled up in his basket, sound asleep.

Again I was forced to wonder whether my imagination was playing tricks with me. But no: there *had* been a light when I looked out of my window; and the light *had* been turned off by the time I got downstairs: of this I was certain. Now a man named Griffiths, who had built the house about a hundred years ago, had gone bankrupt and then committed suicide—in the study, it was said. Our immediate predecessors in the house always maintained that they had seen his ghost; but neither Father nor I had ever done so, and I had not believed a word of their story. I searched for a rational explanation, and I soon found one.

I summoned an electrician from Haslemere to examine the switch. He discovered that the connection was loose; a step on the stairs might easily, he said, have connected or disconnected the current. So, as always, the psychic explanation was superfluous.

Or so I thought. But one night about three weeks later I woke with the sensation that again there was someone in the study. I got up, saw the light, went downstairs and, as before, found the room in darkness. The electrician came again and re-examined the switch; impossible, he said, that this time the light could have turned itself either on or

off. I had known the man for some time; he was honest
and competent, and there could be no question of his
lying his way out of a shoddily done job. So now I, the
complete sceptic, found myself forced to the conclusion that
Mr. Griffiths had been reading Father's theological books,
no doubt in expiation of his crime. Mr. Griffiths would have
to be exorcized.

I knew that Ralph Aylmer had once before dealt with a
similar situation in the village—and, it was said, to the
satisfaction of all concerned. Ralph is a mellifluous, the-
atrical priest, tall and good-looking, very High Church,
much given to copes, incense and processing; these seemed
to me the right qualifications for one called upon to under-
take a task such as this: he would undoubtedly impress
a ghost. He readily agreed to come, gratified I believe to
find me taking an interest in church matters.

Nothing was lacking to make the occasion impressive, the
only discordant element being Mrs. Dudge's hat. Ralph, in
all his finery, followed by two servers with a cross and a
censer, emerged from the glade at the end of the garden
and proceeded solemnly towards the french window where
he paused and called for "Peace to this house and all who
dwell in it." Then he entered and crossed the drawing-
room to the study.

I had quite forgotten about Omar, who was in his basket
in the drawing-room. I suddenly noticed him climb out of
it and join the procession, keeping perfect step with Ralph
and looking in his way no less dignified; as he was about to
go through into the study he turned his head, and I could
almost have sworn that he *winked at me.*

In the study Ralph commanded all evil spirits to depart from the house: "Malevolent spirits remember your sentence, remember your judgment, remember the day to be

at hand wherein you will be committed to the punishment prepared for Satan and his angels; and presume not hereafter to exercise any tyranny towards God's people whom Christ hath bought with his precious Blood, and by his Holy Baptism called to be members of his flock. Amen." Then he sprinkled the room with holy water, and the server swung his thurible. Suddenly the silence was broken by a faint sobbing noise which I thought to have come from

the kitchen tap, but which Helen (who had joined us) in-
terpreted as Mr. Griffiths' expression of grief at being evicted
from his comfortable room.

Though Mr. Griffiths was only known to haunt the study,
Ralph was taking no risks. We passed together from room
to room, with a psalm here, a collect there, and incense
everywhere, till duty had been done. The service, which
had taken the best part of three-quarters of an hour, closed
with the Aaronic Blessing, and after it was over Ralph and
Helen stayed to lunch.

I am bound to confess that from this moment on I had
no further trouble from "things that go bump in the night";
I was therefore forced, much against my instincts, to con-
clude that the house really had been haunted and that
Ralph had laid the ghost.

One morning Mrs. Dudge came into the drawing-room and
announced that she did not propose to be called "a nosy
old bitch" by anyone or—and she looked meaningfully
to where Omar lay peacefully sleeping in his basket—or
any*thing*. I sympathized and asked her who had called her
this. She froze and she said she could not rightly say.

"Well, Mrs. Dudge, I'm sorry but I don't quite see how I
can help. What do you want me to do about it?"

She turned her back on me, muttering that she "wouldn't
stand no more of it," and retired to the kitchen.

Now there had always been a remarkable bush telegraph
in Disbourne; I was not therefore surprised when, a couple
of days later, a reporter and photographer arrived from
the *Haslemere Gazette,* saying they had heard that I

had a pet which talked and that they would like to see it. They declined to betray the source of their information, but I had no doubt that it was Mrs. Dudge; Dr. Canning, ignorant bungler though he was, was unlikely to have so blatantly violated medical etiquette.

I told the men that whatever they had heard was almost certainly exaggerated. I said that Omar, like many a parrot or budgerigar, had several times imitated a word or two of English, but that I was certain that he would not do so to order.

"You don't think it would give a message to our readers?"

"I do not. And even if he did, I very much doubt whether it would be printable."

This was a blunder. "Oh, so when it does talk, it says some pretty odd things?" Obviously Mrs. Dudge had not cared to inform the *Haslemere Gazette* what Omar had called her.

By now the men had more or less edged themselves into the drawing-room, where Omar was restlessly prowling up and down. He took one look at them (they were a rather scruffy pair), uttered a short, sharp "peeee" and bolted through his curtains.

"He can't be disturbed," I said. "He's in the lavatory."

The reporters put a great many further questions to me; these I answered as non-committally as I could. But still Omar did not reappear, and they began to grow impatient. "Will it be much longer in the—in the toilet?" one of them asked.

"It's quite impossible to say. I don't really think there's much point in your waiting."

Finally the photographer took matters into his own hands and drew back one of the curtains. I could have told him that he was asking for trouble.

It was obvious at a glance that Omar had been shamming: the sand on his tray was unsullied. But no one likes having his bluff called, and it was equally obvious that he was extremely angry. His trooling soon turned to troating; when I heard the dangerous "Kkgk . . . rrrrrrr" I knew that the worst was about to happen and shouted to the man to get out of the way.

One might as well have told him to dodge a flash of lightning. Omar flew at his legs, and a moment later the wretched pair were running headlong towards their car. In due course a brief paragraph appeared in their paper. It was captioned BANDERSNATCH BITES PHOTOGRAPHER and gave the usual inaccurate and prejudiced account of what had taken place.

Omar must have guessed that Mrs. Dudge was his enemy, for he now declared open war on her. It was not for nothing that *Till Eulenspiegel* was his favourite piece of music, and his "merry pranks" were many and ingenious. Before long, Mrs. Dudge was completely pixillated.

At the time she did not come into the open about what was happening, but a fortnight later, when she gave notice, she told me everything. At first she had not tumbled to it that Omar was responsible. For example, she was *almost* certain that she had lit the gas under the saucepan, yet when she returned a few minutes later from the scullery she found the tap turned off. She was *almost* sure she could not have left that bucket where she must inevitably fall over it. She found it hard to believe that the wind could have blown over her precious vase of chrysanthemums on the window-ledge. She had no recollection whatever of tearing her apron, and so on. Gradually she became suspicious, but proof was always lacking. She began to set little traps, but she was no match for her wily adversary. She hid behind doors and watched through keyholes; but her wheezings and gruntings would have betrayed her presence even to the very hard of hearing, and Omar's hearing was exceptionally acute. She carefully shut doors behind her, unaware that Omar could now open them. She locked Omar out (as she thought) when she went into the garden to get some broccoli; but when she returned she realized that she had in fact locked him *in*. Omar had accepted the challenge: having reduced the kitchen to a battle-field, he had unlatched the window and run off into the garden.

This episode was the straw that broke the camel's back. Mrs. Dudge went; and though in some ways I was not sorry to see the last of her, I was annoyed with Omar. It meant a lot more work for me. Also I was uneasy about the legends she would circulate in the village. This fear was realized; strange rumours soon reached Helen, who came to see me. Mrs. Dudge was telling everyone that my house was haunted by a devil which had deserted Mr. Griffiths and entered Omar. The line she adopted was that "poor Miss Bavistock" ought to be rescued from herself. All this was very tiresome.

Next week the *Haslemere Gazette* contained the following paragraph:

POLTERGEIST AT DISBOURNE
By our special correspondent

Strange goings-on are reported from Latchmere, the home
of Miss Rose Bavistock. Some weeks ago, following upon
the discovery of a poltergeist in the house, Miss Bavistock
called in the Rector of Disbourne, the Rev. Ralph Aylmer,
to exorcize the ghost of Mr. John Griffiths, a stockbroker
who some eighty years ago committed suicide in the house.
It appears that this poltergeist, reluctant to leave the building,
thereupon entered the body of a pet Bandersnatch belonging
to Miss Bavistock. This animal now spends its time smashing
her crockery and hurling obscenities at all who come to the
house: The Gadarene swine, when similarly situated, had at
least the decency to commit suicide; the Bandersnatch, however, shows no inclination to rid Miss Bavistock of its
unwanted presence. We hope to bring a further report from
Disbourne in our next issue.

2

This article led to a number of tiresome letters and telephone calls; I therefore wrote to the Editor, giving him
the facts (or such of them as I considered suitable) and
asking that I might be left in peace.

But one letter that I received interested me. It came from

Rutherton Runyon, whose admirable but all-too-rare telecolour nature programmes Omar and I never missed. He
said that he had a particular interest in bandersnatches
and had once been to Hyrcania to see them in the wild.
It was his opinion that the bandersnatch was a far more
remarkable animal than was generally realized. He asked
how I had managed to acquire my pet, and added that he
had latterly been so much abroad that he had got out of
touch with recent introductions of unusual animals into
this country. Finally he requested permission to come over
and see Omar. I willingly agreed, and in due course he
arrived at my house.

I could never predict Omar's reactions to people, and I
much hoped that he would not choose to be frumious, or
retire to his lavatory for an interminable and bogus session.
"Be nice to him, Omar," I said as I went to the door. "Mr.
Runyon does those programmes on telecolour that we both
enjoy so much." I had got into the habit of talking to Omar
exactly as though he could understand what I was saying.
But you can imagine my astonishment when Omar advanced *on his hind legs* to greet him, held out his right
front paw, and said something that sounded just like "How
do you do?"

Mr. Runyon was completely captivated. Omar came, quite
of his own accord, and seated himself on his knee dittering
softly; but he could not be persuaded to speak again. Mr.
Runyon and I also got on excellently; he seemed to be
delighted when I told him that Omar and I were great
"fans" of his. After we had had a long and interesting talk
together he suddenly said, "Look—you simply *must* let

Omar appear on one of my programmes."

I saw no harm in this; indeed I thought it might be a very instructive experience, and I was only too pleased to be able to repay Mr. Runyon for some of the pleasure he had given me. But I thought it fair to warn him that Omar was not dependable and that he had a rather puckish sense of fun. "But anyhow," I added, "no doubt you will be recording the programme."

"Certainly not! A 'live' programme always provides a more stimulating atmosphere. The contretemps that sometimes occur add spice to the show. I have little doubt that in the excitement Omar will talk for us."

"Well—it's *your* funeral. Don't say I didn't warn you."

When Mr. Runyon came to take his leave, Omar saw him to the door and said what sounded like "Abyssinia."

The date was fixed, and Mr. Runyon rang me up to ask for a picture of Omar for the *Radio Times*. I had to tell him that Omar did not seem to care for photographers and that I had none to give him. "Never mind," he said; "we'll send you a whole sheaf of photographs after the show."

One bitter afternoon in the early spring I took Omar up to the Telecolour Centre. In the train he was good as gold, allowing two small children in the carriage to caress him and suddenly remarking that it was "very cold for the time of the year"; this was the longest remark I had ever heard him make. I admit I was apprehensive; I had noticed, on a number of occasions, that when Omar was more than usually docile he was generally "up to something." I hoped and prayed that he was not going to be frumious on the set.

The programme was to begin with a short film of bandersnatches in their native haunts, taken in Hyrcania by a team of zoologists led by a man named Leonard Pixleigh. I was particularly eager to see this, having never met any bandersnatch other than mine. Omar sat on my lap while it was being shown. Once or twice he looked up at me, and I seemed to read in his eyes a look of sorrow, yet also perhaps of satisfaction that his own lot was so much more fortunate than theirs. "There, but for the grace of God . . . ," he seemed to be saying.

All too soon the film came to an end. "And now," said Runyon, "we have a very special treat for you. . . ." He went on to speak of Omar's career, of his sweet and docile disposition which made him the perfect household pet, and finally of his remarkable gift of speech, "of which I very much *hope*," he concluded, "we may be able to give you a sample before the end of this programme. Many of you will have heard talking parrots and talking budgerigars. But I don't mind betting that none of you has ever heard— has ever even heard *of*—a talking bandersnatch. Even I had never heard of one before. If you have children, go and fetch them. If necessary, get them out of bed. Let them share with you this unique experience. A talking bandersnatch!" And in his excitement he banged on the table with his fist.

Omar, who had no doubt long been conscious that his great moment was approaching, took this as a signal to exchange my lap for Runyon's—a manoeuvre that he executed with a couple of exquisitely calculated leaps. There was dead silence in the studio.

Now Runyon was wearing round his neck one of those pendant microphones that look like a muffin on a string. Omar played with it for a second or two, then suddenly gripped it with his two front paws and, in a voice disastrously like Runyon's, uttered, and twice repeated, a four-letter word which had probably never before polluted the ether and had only relatively recently edged its way into print. Then, before Runyon or any of his team had recovered from the shock, Omar sprang into the air, shot across the

studio, bolted down a long corridor and was lost to sight.

My readers will probably be familiar with the device, often used at the beginning of telecolour programmes, where a "still" is held on the screen for a few seconds while captions are played upon it, and then suddenly "animated." This was precisely what now occurred. For several seconds —though it seemed more like several hours—we all remained rooted to the ground, just like the courtiers in "Sleeping Beauty" when the spell was cast. Then pandemonium broke loose. It was nearly an hour before Omar was recaptured, and four or five of the BBC men received pretty nasty bites in the process.

Naturally I was in no position to take in what viewers were seeing when the fearful words were spoken, or to witness what happened subsequently; for the least I could do was to join in the chase. But a few days later Ralph Aylmer—shocked though he had been, and not a little angry at the notoriety I had brought upon Disbourne (for of course all the papers were full of it for days to come)— was good enough to describe to me what had occurred.

It seems that the cameras had, unfortunately, not yet been directed away from Runyon's face at the moment when Omar made his regrettable contribution to the programme; viewers therefore had no clue that Omar was lurking no more than a foot or so below his producer's chin. True, Runyon's lips were not seen to move when the fateful word was uttered and re-uttered; but experiment showed that, since it contained no labials, it could be spoken with virtually no movement of the lips. And in any case, who else (thought the viewers) could possibly have spoken it?

It happened that the Aylmers had invited some of the choir boys in to see the programme. Helen immediately clapped her hands over the eyes—ears would have been better—of the two boys who were sitting next to her, but the Rector was too shaken to act. Then, before anyone could turn off the set, picture and sound vanished and were almost instantaneously replaced by:

THERE IS A FAULT IN THE TRANSMISSION
PLEASE DO NOT ADJUST YOUR SET

and the soothing strains of "Sheep may safely graze." The Rector had by this time sufficiently recovered to appreciate the appropriateness of the choice.

That evening the BBC received many hundreds of telephone calls of protest and in due course an enormous quantity of letters. And though the papers for the most part actually printed the truth, nobody for a moment believed such a cock-and-bull story. Truth may be stranger than fiction; but this was really stretching credulity *too* far.

Questions were asked in the House, and after seven bishops had sent a joint letter to *The Times* demanding Runyon's instant dismissal, the wretched man, protesting his innocence to the last, was sacked. He was, however, fortunate enough to get a temporary job on a coypu farm in East Anglia; and I must in all fairness add that he bore me no grudge, admitting that I had warned him and that he had ignored my advice. But it was a very expensive lesson for him, and I was deeply distressed at having been the cause of his disgrace.

But I am anticipating. Next morning, every newspaper I could get hold of (I slipped down to the village and was lucky enough to get half a dozen) carried the story of Omar's enormity; for, as I have already said, the majority accepted the story of his guilt. No doubt the reporters were working on the principle that "man bites dog" is more sensational news than "dog bites man"; I mean, the more improbable the story, the greater its news value. Any tele-caster might, in a momentary lapse, have uttered an ill-considered word, and there had from time to time been re-grettable incidents of this kind; but never before had an *animal*—not even a parrot—let himself go in this way. It was news indeed.

I bought some evening papers too. Of these, alone the *Moon,* in its "Late Night Final" (the one that reaches Dis-bourne at 4 p.m.), laid the blame on the unfortunate Runyon—its editor, a well-known nature-lover, refusing to believe an animal guilty of such a lapse of taste. Subse-quently other newspapers, having achieved their objective with their initial shock-headlines, informed their readers of the possibility, then the probability, and finally the certainty that Omar was after all innocent. And so, as I have already said, Runyon was sacked.

By the second day the reporters had managed to get hold of my name and address, and thereafter, for more than a week, Omar and I lived in a state of almost per-petual siege. I muffled the telephone bell with an old bed-sock, and never left the house; fortunately I was well supplied with tinned food, and Omar had to manage (as he thoroughly deserved) without fresh salads and fruit. By choosing my moment carefully I was able to open the door a crack and so take in the bread and milk. I had begged Omar not to go out of doors, but several times he *prestissimo*'d into the garden and put some particularly repellent pressman to flight. Shilling and Penny also did splendid work.

It is impossible to tell how long this persecution might have continued, had not one of the most exciting events of the century directed every line of newsprint, every second of broadcasting, every square inch of telecolour, into a single channel. When I say that I refer to April 5th, all my readers will know what I mean.

Omar and I sat up till 4 o'clock in the morning, glued to our set as the reports came in. We saw Colonel Blacker and Major Dighton walking along one of Schiaparelli's canals as clearly as if they had been walking down Fifth Avenue. We saw them re-enter their space-rocket and take off, then the red Martian landscape recede and shrink into a russet disk as they began their long return to Earth. We saw them in the capsule, eating hot dogs and toasting the President of the United States in champagne. And then, two months later, we shared the world's grief when we heard that the capsule had crashed into the Gulf of Mexico.

I could not resist the feeling that Omar was saying to himself, "Oh how I would like to be the first bandersnatch on Mars!"

Life now continued peacefully and uneventfully at Disbourne. Omar rarely spoke, but there were several occasions on which he did say a word or two—and always apropos. We were very happy together; he was the perfect companion, and I blessed Uncle Robert for having made me such a wonderful present.

I forget just when it was—perhaps a couple of months later—that I received a letter from the London Zoo. They had recently acquired a young female bandersnatch, and they wrote to ask whether I would allow Omar to sire her. They added that in all probability Omar's outbreaks of temper, of which they had read in the papers, were due to frustration; the experience would undoubtedly be beneficial to him. Though I hated the idea of being without him for a week or two, I felt it would be selfish of me to stand in the way of his health and happiness. I also eagerly looked forward to seeing him a proud father. I therefore gave my rather reluctant consent.

Irene (so they called her, pronouncing it "Ireen") was a pretty young creature with winning little ways. I watched Omar enter her cage; he greeted her cordially, licked her coat, sniffed about a bit and then lay down beside her. The omens seemed favourable. It was only when I got home that I realized how terribly dependent I had become upon his company, how much I missed the patter of his little feet about the house.

I came up to London almost every day to see how things were progressing. At first all seemed to be going well; they lay side by side, and I liked to think that they were exchanging gossip about the old days in Hyrcania. But one morning I arrived to find a very different state of affairs:

Irene, said one of the keepers, had come into season and
was attempting to arouse Omar's interest in her. But Omar
was evincing little enthusiasm; frankly, he looked as though
he found her advances distinctly distasteful.

"Don't worry, Ma'am," said the man—his name was
Bert—"It's only a matter of time."

But each day the keepers grew more glum: Omar, they
said, was not being co-operative. I think it was on the
tenth day that I arrived to find Bert with his arm in a sling;
both he and his colleague, Johnny, were out of humour
and uncommunicative. "It's no good," said Johnny. "You
might as well take him home."

Johnny went off to fetch Omar's basket. I opened the
gate of the enclosure and was about to enter when Bert
seized me by the arm. "For God's sake don't do that; you
haven't even got gloves on." "Nonsense," I said. "Omar
won't hurt me," and pushing the man aside I went in. Omar
immediately came up to me and licked my hand. Subsequently I was to appreciate what a magnanimous gesture
this had been on his part.

The basket arrived and was very cautiously slipped
through the gate; Omar climbed into it and pulled the lid
down with his paw. Not until I had pushed the bolts and
snapped the padlock to, did Bert and Johnny dare to join
me. Then, brave enough now that all the danger was over,
they carried the basket for me to the main gates and hailed
a taxi.

This was my first and last attempt to find Omar a mate.

The terrible earthquake that shattered many houses in Teh-

ran and did appalling damage in the villages on the shores
of the Caspian must still be fresh in the memory of most
of my readers. It happened, in a matter of seconds, on
the evening of August 21st, and the first we heard of it
was when the morning papers arrived. (The paper boy,
I may mention in passing, was not in the least afraid of
my dogs and always came up to the door.) The news was
given in giant headlines by the *Daily Express* (I take this
for the news, and *The Times* for the crossword):

SEVERE EARTHQUAKE IN HYRCANIA
Hundreds feared dead, thousands homeless, on Caspian

Actually this was far less than the truth: the final death-roll
was put at almost eighteen thousand.

After breakfast I threw the paper on the sofa and walked
out into the garden; after all, Hyrcania was very far away
and I would have been more concerned by news of a
widow murdered in Haslemere. When I returned, I found
Omar staring at the headlines and looking very dejected;
he seemed to have been crying. "Don't worry, Omar," I
said. "All your relations are up in the mountains. Their
burrows will be perfectly safe." Omar immediately cheered
up.

It was only some time after I had said this that I realized
that I had taken it for granted that Omar had understood
what was written there. It could, of course, have been
mere coincidence: Omar's eyes sometimes watered, and I
was at that time bathing them daily with Optrex. Yet when
dinner-time came he would not touch his food. He looked
at me as if to say, "Send it to Hyrcania. They need it more

than I do." But I might have been imagining things: perhaps it was just that Omar was not hungry.

However, I thought the matter worthy of further investigation. If Omar could talk—even a little, why should he not be able to read at least a few words of English? I could see no reason whatever. So one day, when he was out in the garden, I hid a bowl of grapes under the sofa and wrote on a sheet of paper. "There is something nice for you under the sofa." I then put the sheet on the floor near the french window, where he would be bound to see it as he came in. When he returned he glanced at the sheet as he passed, then went straight to his basket, curled himself up in it and was soon asleep.

So Omar could not read! Yet I still found this hard to credit: his grief had been so patent, his abstinence surely more than coincidental, after he had gazed at those earthquake headlines. Then it occurred to me that perhaps Omar, like many young children, could not read a cursive script (and mine was far from calligraphic). So I rewrote the message in block capitals and placed it on the hearthrug.

When Omar awoke he advanced towards the paper, studied it a second or two, and then made straight for the sofa. A moment later he had dragged the bowl from under it and was eating the grapes. I was now convinced that he could at least read a few words of large-sized print.

As Father was always so fond of saying, I am not at all clever. My mind, such as it is, works very slowly. Once again, it was only when I had had time to consider the matter that I recognized how amazing this new achievement of Omar's was. I had already come to accept the fact that he was able to speak a few words of English and apparently to speak them purposefully; but the possibility of an animal being able to *read* even a single word had never even been proposed before.

I am of course well aware of those circus turns where an animal—no doubt after much flogging and other brutalities—learns to select the correct lettered brick and spell a word, and so on; but that is something quite different. Professor C. Lloyd Morgan, a great authority on animal intelligence, wrote as follows on the subject:

P. G. Hamerton, many years ago [1873], described how, in his own house, a cleverly trained dog would fetch in their right order the letters which spelt the English or German equivalents of common French words, and do other wonderful things. But the owner of the dog (M. du Rouil) admitted that there was a means of *rapport* between them which he was not prepared to divulge. . . . [A trainer of animals] showed Mr. Meehan how a collie would spell his own name and words sent up by the audience by bringing the right letters from an alphabet. The collie went along the letters, picked out the one he needed, and brought and laid it before the footlights. But the trick was really simple. His master carried his gloves in his hand. A little twitch of the gloves as the dog passed the particular letter wanted was the cue. The well-trained animal took in the slightest stir of the gloves with the corner of his eye. This dog even played a game of cards—and won. . . .[1]

All this demonstrated the extraordinary delicacy of perception of the dogs concerned, and their ability to connect a particular gesture with a particular mode of behaviour; but there was never the faintest suggestion that letters conveyed any meaning. Never, in the whole long history of man, had there been an animal which could associate the letters C A T with a feline domestic animal.

Now Rutherton Runyon, in spite of the cruel trick Omar had played upon him, still kept in touch with me and had more than once expressed a keen desire to see Omar again; I felt sure he would be interested in this new development, and I therefore invited him over. He arrived, smelling

[1] *Harmsworth Natural History,* vol. 1, p. 97.

rather strongly of coypu but looking as handsome as ever, and went straight up to Omar, who greeted him very cordially. Did I read, in Omar's eyes, a sense of shame and of penitence? It is so easy for the imagination to find what it would wish to find. At all events, there was not the slightest indication that Rutherton (he has asked me to call him that) harboured any grievance over the unhappy episode that had come between them.

I told Rutherton exactly what had taken place, and he was as excited as I was. "We may be on the threshold of a discovery of unbelievable importance," he said. "I entirely agree with you that if Omar can say even two or three words *purposefully,* then he is almost certainly able to say a great deal more than he cares to admit. And if he could really read those headlines and that message you wrote for him—I say *if*—then he must certainly be able to read any ordinary text in block capitals. I agree with you that it does look as though he could, but obviously he must be more scientifically tested. We simply *must* keep in touch."

We went out into the garden, leaving Omar indoors, to discuss the best way to proceed. For if Omar could speak and read, was it not more than probable that he could understand every word we said? Rutherton agreed with me that I ought to "have it out" with Omar: to tell him straight that I knew he could understand what I said, and that he was perfectly capable of replying if he wanted to. In other words, I was to call his bluff. But, all too soon, it was time for Rutherton to return to his coypus; before leaving, however, he was good enough to sign for me a photograph of him which I had got from the *Radio Times*. He leant out of his car as he drove off and cried, "Don't forget! *Keep in touch!*"

I don't like having things hanging over me, so that same evening I called Omar to me and told him that I knew he could read, could understand what I said, and could answer me if he so wished. He stared at me blankly. I tried once more: *"Please,* Omar! I *know* you can speak if you want to."

But it was useless. And indeed Omar looked so vacantly at me that once again I began to have doubts.

That autumn was one of the loveliest that I can ever remember; it must really have been something rather special, because I am not easily affected by the beauties of nature. The situation with Omar having reached a kind of deadlock, I found myself again taking a greater pleasure in my two alsatians; day after day I went with them for long walks through the golden woods. It was not exactly intentionally that I thus left Omar more than usual to his own devices; but after a time I became conscious that he was feeling rather neglected, and there were even little signs of jealousy. This was something quite new: until now he had taken it for granted that he was king of my household. I deliberately made no effort to humour him. It was some time since he had last spoken, and I had not had any fresh evidence of his being able to read; he had successfully evaded several little "traps" that I had set for him. I thought it possible that he might attempt to re-establish his position by some further demonstration of his prowess.

At the beginning of November there was a sudden spell

of exceptional cold. One afternoon Omar came in from the
garden, his fur covered with snow; he was shivering and
looked dejected. I dried him down and pulled his basket
up to the fire, but he continued to mope and to trool, and I
could not get him to eat more than a few grapes. When three
days had passed and he seemed no better, I sent for
Mr. Paterson, the Haslemere vet.

Naturally Paterson had never before seen a bandersnatch,
but he had a wide general experience of animals. He suspected a mild attack of pleuro-pneumonia, wrote a pre-
scription, and urged me to keep him warm and, above
all, away from draughts. As he said the word "draughts,"
I could almost have sworn that Omar winked an eye at me.

By Christmas Omar was well on the way to recovery;
but his eyes lacked lustre, his fur its gloss. He moved
mostly in bottom gear, and did not seem to trust himself
up a wall. Had he been a human being, one would have
recommended sea air and a good tonic. On December 30th,
just after the clock had struck eleven—a moment that I
am never likely to forget—I said to Omar, "If only I knew
what I could give you to get you right again!"

Omar looked me squarely in the face and said, "I
believe a bottle or two of *Châteauneuf du Pape* '67 might
do the trick."

Part III
DIXIT

I

"My dear Miss Resker . . . Tobermory can speak our language with perfect correctness."

"Tobermory," *by Saki*

"Yes," said Omar, "(—*do* turn that machine off!) You were perfectly right. I can speak English at least as fluently as you can, and indeed more grammatically. I can understand everything you say, although you have a tendency to mumble. And I can read print; but I still find a slovenly cursive hand difficult—yours especially.

"I have often considered telling you all this, but what guarantee had I that you would not put the information to improper use? What guarantee indeed have I now—except that I shall request you to promise never to betray my secret without my permission? If you do not do this, then I shall never speak again. Not a soul would believe your story, and you would merely make yourself look ridiculous. Will you promise?"

What else could I do?

"I mean *no one*," Omar continued, "not even your friend

Mr. Runyon. In fact, especially not Mr. Runyon. I like him, and I am sorry I lost him his job. But he is not to be trusted; no zoologist could be trusted with so sensational a secret. Though I don't for a moment believe that anyone would accept his word either, none the less it is better to be on the safe side.

"We will speak more of all this tomorrow. But now I am tired; and as you know I am not yet well. I think as I have already said, that some Rhône wine, or failing that a nice red burgundy such as Clos de Vougeot or Nuits St. Georges (but choose the vintage carefully), would be of the greatest help to my full recovery. Be so good as to order some in Haslemere in the morning—and perhaps a small tin of caviare also. Then tomorrow evening we will celebrate—and talk afterwards. And now, good night!"

Omar jumped off my lap, moved slowly towards his basket, curled himself up in it and closed his eyes. A few minutes later he appeared to be asleep.

But for me, sleep was impossible. Though Omar's confession had not exactly been unexpected, yet when he made it—when I actually heard him speak in fluent English —I was completely stunned. All previous reports of similar performances had either been deliberately falsified or inadequately substantiated. No properly authenticated record existed of an animal speaking rationally—even no more than a few consecutive words.

But here—and I recalled the words of Saki—was indisputable evidence of "a discovery beside which the invention of gun-powder, of the printing-press, and of steam locomotion were inconsiderable trifles." Had he been writing fifty years later, he would doubtless also have included the atom bomb and the marvels of the space age. And I— I alone, was the guardian of this stupendous secret. Had I the right to keep it to myself? Suppose Omar were to die before others had heard him speak, would anyone believe my testimony? Tape-recordings? They would be denounced as a fake. Yet I had given my word that I would not betray him. I felt that I must make every effort to persuade him to let me talk to Rutherton; with his wide experience he would know how to advise me. It was an intolerable burden to bear alone.

Next morning Omar took not the slightest notice of me. I spoke to him but he would not answer, and I began to wonder whether the events of the previous evening had not been a mere figment of my imagination. In the afternoon I drove into Haslemere and bought half a dozen bottles of Corton '67, strongly recommended by my wine merchant. He was surprised at the extravagance of my order; though I am no teetotaller, I usually content myself with a bottle or two of the kind of Beaujolais that Omar was later to dismiss scornfully as "red ink." I felt, however, that at the moment I must do everything possible to humour him. I also bought a tin of caviare and some pretty expensive hothouse grapes.

In the winter I often have my dinner on a tray by the drawing-room fire. I prepared Omar's and placed it on the sofa opposite me, the caviare spread on small thin slices of bread and butter, and beside it a saucer into which I intended pouring his wine. Then—and I don't really quite know why—I sounded the gong, just as Martha always did when Father was alive, and brought in my own tray. Omar had still not broken his silence; but as I was putting the corkscrew into the bottle, he suddenly did the most brilliant *trompe-l'oreille* imitation of a cork popping. We both started laughing, and the ice was broken.

I was about to pour some wine into his saucer when he said, "No—in a wine-glass, please! I have been practising and I can hold one with a thin stem. Good wine like this (and I commend your choice) must be drunk as a gentleman would drink it."

Half in a dream, I went and fetched a glass. My hand trembled so much that I spilled a little wine on the carpet as I poured it out. I apologized for my clumsiness.

"No matter!" said Omar. "After all it's not my Axminster. Well—here's to your very good health!"

Dinner at an end, Omar said, "Now I want to talk seriously. You will perhaps have been wondering why I have suddenly decided to take you into my confidence. There are several reasons. First, this illness of mine has been something of a shock to me. I realized that I might die, and so carry my secret with me to the grave. That would be a pity, because it is of considerable scientific interest. Then there are certain things I would like you to teach me. For instance, I want to learn to write, and I find it difficult to do so without help. I want to learn to use a typewriter; though I have once or twice experimented with yours while you were out, this surreptitious use of it is frustrating.

"But far more important: I want, so far as is humanly—

I mean, animally—possible, to make the experiment of adapting myself to the human way of life. I want to eat at table, to wear clothes, to sleep in a bed and not in that ridiculous basket. I want to use the lavatory and not this unhygienic and embarrassing tin tray (though I bless you for rigging up the curtains). I want—now that they have

found a cure for lung cancer—to smoke cigarettes and sometimes of an evening a small cigar. I would like to be able to do around the house some at least of those jobs that are expected of a man: to mend a fuse, for instance; hang a picture or clean a pair of shoes. Carrying coals will, I fear, always remain beyond my powers; but perhaps I could compensate for this by learning to cook.

"As for the longer-term future—well, we must wait and see. Let us at all events pass the rest of this winter quietly together. I am thankful that you have got rid of that fearful old gas-bag, Mrs. Dudge; we shall be alone in the house, but we shall have to be careful. The time will perhaps come when I shall allow you to discuss my affairs with others, but it has not come yet.

"I like the quiet life. You have already subjected me to the vulgar publicity of telecolour, though I think I have assured myself against a repetition of that indignity. But I was hoist with my own petard, landing myself with a notoriety that I had not foreseen. I do not want to end up in a fairground as 'the Talking Bandersnatch,' or as 'todays special guest' at a chimps' tea-party.

"So let us enjoy one another's company for a while. I will not be an unreasonable burden to you, though from now on I shall make greater demands on your time, as also on your purse. I observe, however, that in spite of the Labour Government (I am a Liberal) you appear to be still in reasonably comfortable circumstances. I propose shortly to write a brief account of my experiences before coming to Disbourne; this will, I am sure, be of interest to you. By the by—next time you go to Haslemere I would like an oil-painting outfit; I think painting might be rather in my line.

"I see it is nearly midnight. Now you may turn on the telecolour again, and we will drink to the New Year together. It may well prove a very eventful year for us both. Well, *I* seem to have done most of the talking so far tonight. But after all, in my fifteen months here I have not spoken more than a dozen words until yesterday evening. I have a good deal of leeway to make up."

Big Ben sounded and, half in a dream, I clicked my glass against Omar's. "Here's the skin off your nose!" he said; "—a vulgar toast which I recollect having read in an Edwardian *Punch.*"

"And here's the skin off yours," I said, accepting the gambit.

It was 2 o'clock before we finally went to bed, and our discussion—for I was now allowed to join in—covered a wide field. I was amazed at the incredible breadth of Omar's knowledge; it seemed that he had merely to skim through the pages of a book to absorb its contents, and every word that he had heard uttered remained for ever fixed in his memory.

"Yes," he said—"it is a case of *Omar sapiens* rather than *homo sapiens,* I fear. I don't wish to boast, but false modesty is pointless: I think it safe to say that I have a better brain than any man or woman in England. If I do decide to put my talents at the disposal of the country, it will probably be because I can no longer tolerate the monstrously inefficient way in which it is being run. I wonder if they would ever make me Prime Minister; then I might really be able to do something . . ."

I took an almost lethal dose of sleeping tablets; yet for a long time I lay awake, turning over and over in my mind the extraordinary revelations I had heard. When finally sleep came, it was tormented by wild dreams: of Omar as Prime Minister, saving the country; of Omar as President of England; of Omar as Pope, finding the Triple Crown so many sizes too large; of Omar, Emperor of the Universe. . . .

There now began a wholly new relationship between Omar and myself. Each morning I gave him lessons, working to a time-table that we had drawn up together. It so happened that I still had in the house certain relics of my childhood, and some of these now came in very useful. My old cot served him admirably for a bed, and in my high baby-chair he was able to sit beside me when we ate in the dining-room. Although, as he well knew, eating with the fingers was still a common practice in many parts of the Middle East, he insisted upon learning to use knife, fork and spoon. I purchased a doll's house canteen and tea-set and other little household objects suited to his size. And it was Omar himself who managed to gnaw a saucer-sized hole in a piece of 3-ply, so making a lavatory seat that he could use without risk of drowning.

But over clothes we failed completely. Unfortunately I am hopeless with a needle and thread, and there was no one whom I could take into my confidence; I was therefore obliged to buy a large golliwog for the sake of its blue trousers and red jacket. But these fitted none too well, and Omar, after studying himself in the glass, came to the conclusion that he was really better off without them. "They make me look a perfect imbecile," he said. "So long as it doesn't embarrass *you,* I'd rather stay as I am." I assured him that it did not. But to tell the truth, it did—rather. Now that Omar had become so nearly human, the natural nakedness of the animal was transformed into a nudity that it was at times hard to overlook.

For some time past Omar had been able to walk reasonably

well, though very slowly, on his hind legs—indeed I had ceased to think of them as *hind* legs, for his fore legs and fore paws had virtually become arms and hands. But when he wanted to cover a distance quickly, he still had to run on all fours; and of this he was heartily (though quite unnecessarily) ashamed. His posture when erect was rather curious, his chest and behind projecting much as did the bosom and bustle of an Edwardian soprano on the concert platform. Omar was aware of this and it worried him; one evening when we were looking together at an "old crocks" air display on telecolour, he remarked of a TSR 2 taking off, "Do you know, it rather reminds me of ME!"

Long before Omar was able to write he had learned to paint. I cannot claim to have taught him—my contribution was merely to provide him with the necessary equipment; in any case, instruction is today quite unnecessary, indeed often positively harmful in that it may curb originality and interfere with the development and flowering of natural genius. A number of Omar's paintings, and some experimental sculpture made out of soldered caviare tins, were shown at the Tryout Galleries in the autumn. They were much praised by the critics (who were irresistibly reminded of the work of Giotto, the youngest of the three Bonifazios, and Jokeman Polaxe), and his "Frumious Bandersnatch" was acquired off the walls for the Tate. In fact, so much interest was aroused in this "brilliant young Hyrcanian, of whom we shall certainly hear more," as the art critic of the *Moon* wrote, that I was much pestered by the Tryout Galleries to produce him or at least make his address available to admirers.

Omar was interested in music; he had a pleasant voice and a good ear. He felt at one time that he ought to learn a musical instrument, but it was difficult to think of a suitable one. Since his fingers could only stretch a fourth on the keyboard, the piano was more or less out of the question; at a later date the Master of the Queen's Musick did in fact compose, especially for him, a "Hyrcanian Serenade" which was written almost entirely in minor thirds and demanded nothing that was physically beyond his powers, but Omar never became proficient at the instrument. I trained his voice—which was a very light tenor— and sometimes on an evening we would run through the simpler songs of the *Dichterliebe* together. "I think I might have learned to play the nasal flute," he once said. But he saw quite clearly that his time was really better employed upon those arts such as painting and sculpture, which make no demands upon either technique or discipline and are therefore so ideally suited to the amateur.

Over learning to write, Omar was slower than I would have expected; it used to make me smile to see him trying to grasp the pen between his plump, black little fingers. But in the end he developed quite a pleasant Italic cursive, joined the Society for Italic Handwriting, and won first prize in a *Daily Telegraph* competition for the under tens. We wrote "Aged 8" on his entry, thinking that the judge might not consider "Aged 3" credible. I still treasure the first word he ever wrote:

and one or two of his early exercises—for example, a page upon which he had written a dozen times

But the majority of his writings, including the following autobiographical fragment which he addressed to me, are now in the British Museum. This account of his early days in Hyrcania, his brief visit to Arabia, and his time in London before joining me at Disbourne, was written on my typewriter, which he mastered long before he could properly control a pen; it was subsequently published in the *Observer*'s "Weekend Review."

MY EARLY LIFE
by Omar Bandersnatch

I was born in the Province of Mazandaran (southern Hyrcania), not very far from Parus.

I was the youngest of three, my brother Khosrau and his twin sister Shirin being some seven months older than I. My father had disappeared about a fortnight after I was born. He had gone down to the sturgeon fisheries to try to bring back some caviare (which all bandersnatches love), and he never returned; no doubt he was shot. Mother, knowing the risk, had begged him not to go, but he would not listen; after that she never touched caviare again. Khosrau, who was a bit of a dare-devil, would sometimes disobey Mother's orders and raid the warehouse, and then we three would have a sort of dormitory feast, finding double pleasure in the forbidden fruit.

Mother was a most charming and capable woman, and she brought us up well. She had a genius for languages, and though we would chatter away among ourselves in Bandersnatch all day, we were always made to talk Persian at supper; "You never know," she used to say, "when it may not come in very useful." Mother had learnt Persian from listening to the woodcutters. There was nothing she enjoyed more than concealing herself in the branches of the tree under which they ate their frugal midday meal of rice,

fruit and *dugh;* thus she picked up titbits of local gossip
or added a new word or a striking phrase to her already
extensive vocabulary. These novelties she would introduce
casually at supper the same evening, telling us to memorize
them for future use. For example, she might suddenly say,
"Really that road to Parus is *long as the entrails of Omar";*
and then she would pause and look round to see the effect
it had on us children. Of course we always applauded.

Some time before I was born, Mother had come upon a
copy of Sadi's *Gulistan* which must have been dropped by
one of the woodcutters. "I know I really ought to have left
it where they could find it again," she said; "but the temptation was too great." Before long she had succeeded in un-
ravelling the script, and one of our greatest pleasures was
hearing her read aloud from it in the summer evenings
before the light failed. We bandersnatches have excellent
night-sight for general purposes, but she could not read
print in the dark; in time, however, she had got certain
passages from it by heart and, so Khosrau told me, would
recite it in the long winter evenings. You humans consider
it wonderful that the trilingual Rosetta stone enabled scholars
to decipher Egyptian hieroglyphics; but how far more astonishing was Mother's achievement!

Bandersnatches live together in small communities, and
though we can climb we do not make our homes in trees.
In our "housing estate" there were some twenty families
distributed over two or three acres of the forest. Our burrow was charmingly situated beneath a bank covered with
primroses and violets, and "quite over-canopied with luscious
woodbine"—for these slopes of the Elburz are, I believe,
very like certain parts of England—and was generally considered to be the best designed and best constructed of all
those in our part of the forest. It had been in the family

for several hundred years, but Father had modernized it and improved the drainage, stopping what had once, I gather, been a bad leak in the roof of our winter quarters at the remotest end of the burrow.

The entrance was so artfully contrived that no one could possibly have found it, though of course the woodcutters knew where it was; they saw our comings and goings, but they were our friends (or so we then believed). We did them no harm; and since our fur was of no commercial value, and our flesh considered inedible, they left us in peace. One of the men—an amiable fellow with a splendid black moustache and only one eye—used to call out "Hullo, Joey!" whenever he saw me, and sometimes he would give me a few grapes left over from their meal.

Of course, I shall never forget that awful day when I was caught by Professor Pixleigh. It was the 3rd of *Rajab* by our calendar, and we were just finishing luncheon, which in the summer we always ate on the grass outside the burrow entrance. Actually it was a rather special occasion, because it was Khosrau's and Shirin's first birthday and our good neighbours the Khayyams had joined us; moreover Khosrau had defied Mother and gone down to the sturgeon fisheries to fetch caviare, which we children had eaten in secret as an *hors d'oeuvre*.

The woodcutters, who took their meal earlier than we did, had already restarted work and everything seemed perfectly normal when Mother suddenly said, "I *smell* something." We all remained still, and little Suleika Khayyam said, "I *hear* something." So did we all, now: it was a faint whirring noise, and later I knew it to have been Pixleigh's photographer telefilming us at our meal.

"I'll go and have a look," I said.

Mother cried out, "Careful, Ahmad!" (for that is my real name).

Alas! I was young and impetuous and trusting; when my friend the amiable woodcutter called out, "Come along, Joey!" and held out a bunch of grapes, I ran towards him. But just before I reached him, a man sprang out from behind an oak tree and with a very cleverly aimed thrust caught me in the meshes of a large butterfly-net.

It was all over in a second. Before I could even think of trying to bite my way out, I was swung into the air, rammed

into a stout sack and carried to a car which had been left three or four hundred yards down the road. Of course I cried for help, and Mother and Khosrau came running up. I heard them attacking my captor's legs, and they certainly must have succeeded in biting him. But the woodcutters—the very men whom we had always utterly trusted—beat them off with sticks. I could see nothing, of course, of what was happening, and I have always feared that Mother may have been hurt. If it took me some time to become reconciled to humans, you will understand why: I can never forgive those Judases for their treachery, and when I heard them receiving their blood-money I felt quite sick.

I was soon to learn the purpose of Professor Pixleigh's hunting expedition: he had been asked by his old friend the Akhoond of Juddi—one of those oil billionaires with a pocket-handkerchief sheikhdom on the Persian Gulf—to obtain a young bandersnatch as a pet for his son, Prince Mahmud. I was flown to Juddi in a stiflingly hot plane of the Akhoond's flight and taken along innumerable gilded corridors of the royal Palace to the Prince's apartments.

It was the hour of the siesta, and Mahmud was lying half-naked on a silver bed, watching Asiavision. He was a plump, self-indulgent, odious twelve-year-old boy who—I soon discovered—wanted something to bully, not to love. Oh how I wish my teeth had then been as sharp, and my jaws as strong as they are now! But I was still only a cub. However, I think I gave a pretty good account of myself. When Mahmud tried to pull my whiskers I flew at his cheek, and when he kicked out at me I dodged behind him and bit his bottom. You humans don't know what you miss by not biting one another more; there are few pleasures comparable to that of getting one's teeth into a really succulent piece of unloved flesh.

Of course the spoilt child started yelling, whereupon a couple of the palace guards rushed in. I looked for a way of escape, but the room was air-conditioned and the windows shut. I ran up the wall and for a time eluded them. However, in the end I was caught and trussed and taken to the stables where I remained, half-starved and three-quarters suffocated, until Professor Pixleigh arrived to take me away. That was the end of my brief connection with royalty.

Professor Pixleigh was a dapper, bouncy little man of about forty-five, with sandy hair and freckles; he rather reminded me of a young fox I used to know in Mazandaran. What I now write about him I only learned at a later date. Fundamentally he was a nice chap, but he had been spoilt by too much success too early in life. He had written a number of books about his experiences with animals. *Elephant in the House* (40,000 copies and numerous translations) was followed by *Elephant at Sea, Elephant in Clover* and others, all of which sold well. *No Ostriches for Miss Blandish* described, very movingly, the unsuccessful attempt of a young Englishwoman to establish an ostrich farm in a disused gasworks in Hampstead.

But it was *Into Bed with an Alligator,* and the libel suit that followed upon its publication, which made the Professor a small fortune and his name a household word. (Of course you will have read all about it in the papers at the time.) The reviewer of the *Moon,* after describing the book as "a lively piece of fiction," said that the photographs which illustrated it were "fakes; I knew that stuffed alligator well when it was for sale in the Fulham Road." Pixleigh immediately sued the *Moon* and its minion, and doubtless the matter would have been settled without great fuss or publicity had not the judge ruled for a demonstration to be made for the benefit of the jury. A large double bed was brought into court, and Professor Pixleigh, in a very expensive pair of pink-and-white-striped silk pyjamas (which he maintained were an essential part of the act), climbed in on one side. Then an unmistakably live, and lively, and very large female alligator was produced. She surveyed the crowded courtroom with an air of infinite boredom, stared at the judge and yawned a yard wide, snapped her jaws at the jury, and then gave the bed and its occupant a look of recognition.

In the tense silence a voice suddenly rang out from the public gallery, "Come along, Gertrude! Time for beddi-bye!" It was, as every reader of *Into Bed with an Alligator* well knew, the operational command by which Pixleigh brought his bedmate to his side.

"Order!" shouted the judge, "or I'll clear the court."

Pixleigh looked worried, but the alligator did not hesitate for a moment; she had received and registered the message, instinctively she acted upon it. Shuffling her vast shanks, she waddled across the floor towards the bed, moored herself alongside it like a great river barge berthing at a wharf, lifted herself up by her front paws, and with a great sigh and a great groan heaved herself into bed beside her lord and master.

There was a sensation in court which even the judge made no attempt to silence. But when order again prevailed, he was heard to inquire of the defendant whether he would care to change places with the plaintiff. Counsel for the defence conferred with his client a moment and then said, "No m'Lud. My client, with your Lordship's permission, would prefer to remain where he is."

Pixleigh was awarded £10,000 damages, and received publicity that was worth at least treble that sum. Everything he now wrote turned to gold. *The Love Life of a Louse* was serialized in a popular Sunday newspaper and sold 65,000 copies before publication. Its successor, *The Love Life of the Coleoptera,* was in even greater demand, though many of the teenagers who purchased it were disappointed by its contents.[1]

Such, then, was the Professor into whose clutches I had fallen; he was, as I have already stated, at heart a decent fellow. It goes without saying that I bit him at first, but he took it in good part and was never vindictive. So I decided to make the best of a bad job. When he returned to London in September he took me with him and installed me in his very comfortable Hampstead house, soon giving me the complete run of it and of the garden. He had a large circle of friends, and it was not too long before I had acquired a working knowledge of English from listening to their conversation.

There were many occasions when I would dearly have liked to join in—especially when Pixleigh ("Len" to his friends) was talking arrant nonsense about Hyrcania in general and bandersnatches in particular; I could hardly contain myself when he referred to my mother as "a mangy old bitch" who "pretended" to come to my assistance. But I saw the danger: I would be made a nine-days' wonder. "Omar—the Talking Bandersnatch." Fuss and publicity; thousands of people goggling at me. . . . It is strange to think that two such trivial matters as Professor Tanker's absurd exaggerations and an open french window, were to be the ultimate provocations which made me give myself away—though only of course to a very limited extent.

Pixleigh was usually out for a good deal of the day. Before leaving, he would prepare my plate of grapes, bananas and lettuce and say, "Back at seven, Omar. Be a good boy! Keep the burglars away!"—just as though he knew I could understand what he was saying. His long absences were invaluable

[1] "The Coleoptera" was the name of a group of pop singers who won a certain notoriety at that time. (Ed.)

to me, because they gave me time and opportunity to study
the books in his splendid library. Mother had given me a hint
or two as to how to tackle a printed script, and before my
capture I had begun to read her precious volume of Sadi; I
now tried to apply the same principles to English. At first it
was very difficult; but I worked at it hour after hour, until
finally I had made enough progress to be able to get the gist
of almost anything that caught my interest. This included,
besides zoological works, the novels of Dickens and Jane
Austen.

I had some awkward moments, though. For instance, there
were three heavy folio volumes called *Mammals of the World*
which I particularly wanted to study. With great difficulty I
got the first volume down from the shelf; but when the time
came for me to put it back again I found that I simply couldn't
manage it. So I had to leave it on the floor. Pixleigh returned,
saw the book lying there, and said to me in a hearty voice,
"Hullo, Omar! Been looking up your family history?" How
astonished he would have been had I answered, "Yes, Pixleigh;
that is exactly what I was doing!" But once again I refrained.

Another situation was created by my acquiring a taste for
alcohol. Pixleigh lived well and had an excellent cellar; as a
"friend" of his said one evening when he was out of the room,
"Len is a bit of a bore, but he has the best cellar in Hampstead." I longed to sample those pretty coloured liquids which
made sad men suddenly gay and dull men almost amusing, and
soon the chance came my way. A man named Butterfield—a
zoologist of some repute, I gathered—was having a drink with
Pixleigh. The conversation turned inevitably upon bandersnatches, and how we were a mysterious kind of missing link
between the rhino and the horse. Then Butterfield said,
"There's an old legend that bandersnatches become alcoholics

if they get the chance. Have you ever tried giving Omar a drink?"

"No," replied Pixleigh, "but I'll do so now." And fetching a saucer he poured into it a couple of tablespoonfuls from a bottle labelled "MADEIRA. FINEST OLD SERCIAL" and offered it to me. May Allah forgive me! I tasted it—and found it perfectly delicious.

"Like another?" said Pixleigh, waving the bottle at me. I took an extra lick at the empty saucer to make my answer clear, and the dose was repeated. In fact I could have done with a third, but Butterfield stopped him as he was about to pour it out: "Don't overdo it," he said; and no doubt he was right, for I was quite tipsy already and might easily have given myself away by saying "Cheerio!" as I drank it. I felt extraordinarily light-hearted and longed to "show off"; in fact, when Butterfield said, "There's your next book, Len: *Boozing with a Bandersnatch*," I could hardly refrain from joining in the conversation. However, I contented myself with a few elegant pirouettes and somersaults and a jolly scamper up the walls and round the cornice. My antics were much applauded, and it was generally agreed that the old legend must be true. I too began to fear that it might be.

So far so good. But next day, while Pixleigh was out, I had an irresistible urge to sample a drink to which some of Pixleigh's friends were much attached—I mean whisky. At that time I was still very clumsy with my "hands," and I had the utmost difficulty in manipulating the decanter, which I was terrified of breaking. Finally I coaxed some of the liquid into the saucer, but when I squirted the soda-water siphon, as I had often seen them do, I splashed the whole neighbourhood including several of Pixleigh's books. Worse still: when I tried to drink the stuff I found it so disgusting that I simply couldn't

get it down. Then, before I had got the place properly ship-shape, Pixleigh returned—a good deal earlier than I had been led to expect.

He seemed surprised but said nothing. At that moment he was very preoccupied with the question as to whether or not he could face the discomfort of joining an expedition to the Himalaya to search for the Abominable Snowman; temporarily he had rather lost interest in bandersnatches. Yet, looking back on these two episodes, I feel he was much at fault for not deducing what had happened. He knew, had he troubled to think about it, that on neither occasion could his "daily" have been there at the time, because though she came every evening she was only able to manage three mornings a week. And no one else had the key. Therefore I, and I only, could have moved that book and upset that soda-water.

It is this lack of imagination that has prevented Pixleigh from becoming a really first-rate zoologist. That, and his conceit. He *knew* that an "animal" could not read a book or pour out a whisky-and-soda; so he dismissed the matter from his mind. You, with far less actual knowledge, had a more flexible approach. It would never have occurred to Pixleigh that Saki's *Tobermory* might have been fact (as I feel sure it was) rather than fiction, because such an assumption cut right across his preconceptions; *you* took nothing for granted. And that is why I am glad it was you, and not Pixleigh, who finally discovered my secret.

One evening when Pixleigh was entertaining a few friends, I learnt that he had finally made up his mind to go in pursuit of the Abominable Snowman. "Soon," he said, "I shall be too old for these rough trips. I don't really care a dam whether or not we find the creature; but I *would* like to see the Himalayas once again before I die—and preferably at someone else's expense. Of course, I shall have to get rid of Omar . . . I suppose I'd better try the Zoo first. But I'll make them give me a hundred for him: he's a cute little beggar—worth every penny of that, and more."

"I'll give you fifty if you don't get a better offer," chimed in a very self-important little man named Weaver.

"Any advance on fifty?" said Pixleigh. "How about you, John? Or you, Michael? Come along, Christopher—just the thing for your zoo!"

But the bidding had stopped at fifty. "Well, my offer stands," Weaver repeated. "You may be glad enough to take it later on."

I soon had reason to fear that he might be, for not long afterwards a man from the Zoo came to look at me and suggested that £40 would be a fair price. Pixleigh said he would rather *give* me away than be swindled, and showed him the door. Then I learned that he was going to approach Interfauna, with whom he had had some satisfactory dealings in the past; but I think he was as surprised as I was when Interfauna's representative agreed almost immediately to the figure proposed. "Omar will be very handy for a little job that's just come our way," he said. "Canadian millionaire with plenty of money to throw around, so we might as well split the profits. You've done me some good turns in the past."

"I don't want Omar to go just anywhere. Make sure he gets a nice home."

"Trust me."

As you know, Interfauna made no inquiries whatever about you. That firm is something of a racket. It may interest you to learn that your uncle paid a thousand dollars for me, so that it made nearly three hundred per cent profit on the deal.

I was only at Interfauna's for ten days, so I cannot really speak of it with much authority. I have few complaints beyond the company I was obliged to keep, and the unavoidable lack of freedom and of privacy. The cages were small but they were kept clean; the food was suitably chosen, well prepared and sufficient in quantity. The room was warm and free from draughts—which is more than can be said of your drawing-room. But my neighbours . . . ! For ten whole days and nights I found myself next a disgusting buzzard, quite un-house-trained, who spent his time exchanging dirty stories with a vulture as loathsome as himself; they saw that it revolted me and did it quite deliberately. I could only understand a fragment of what they said, but their obscene gestures spoke more plainly than words. Then the caracal—a pretty creature, I admit, but with table-manners that would disgrace an Italian peasant. And the shindy made, night and day, by those parakeets I shall never forget so long as I live; they ought to have issued us with ear-plugs and sleeping pills.

Though I knew that I might well be going out of the frying-pan into the fire, I was thankful when the day came for me to be driven down to Disbourne. And I am glad that a fortunate chance enabled me to spit at the buzzard as I was being carried out to the car. It was almost the only time in my life when I have been seriously tempted to use my "secret weapon." As you know, we bandersnatches have this "scent gland," but no member of our family has used it since the reign of Shah Abbas the Great (of blessed memory). Mother once said, "I will disown any of my children who do this filthy thing, whatever the provocation. In time, if we persevere, Nature will rid us of our unwanted gland, as she has ridden man of his unwanted tail. You can read all about it in the works of Darwin, I believe."

I feel that I owe you some sort of an apology for my rough treatment of you when I first arrived at Disbourne. I did what I did to test you, of course, and as soon as I found that you were the right owner for me I desisted. I was deeply impressed by your courage in coming unarmed like that into my enclosure. I was struck, too, by the fact that you clearly realized that I had *deliberately* changed my attitude towards you. In short, I saw that you possessed possibilities that I had not yet found in a human being. That moment was, I now know, the beginning of the "beautiful friendship" that Interfauna so rashly promises to all its clients.

2

Such was the account that Omar wrote for me, rather fumblingly, on my old typewriter. He used often to speak about Mazandaran: "That was us, of course, and the Khayyams, whom you saw in Mr. Pixleigh's film. I don't suppose you recognized me; I was a good deal younger then. I had seen it often before; but it upsets me every time, and I think that was probably the reason why I behaved so badly to poor Mr. Runyon. Oh! how I wonder what has happened to Mother and Khosrau and Shirin—and to little Suleika Khayyam. Shall I ever see any of them again?

"By the way, you have no doubt guessed by now that it was I who was your ghost in the study. I used to seize the opportunity, after you had gone to bed, to get on with my reading. I couldn't help smiling to myself when old Ralph Aylmer went through all that mumbo-jumbo; and it was I too, of course, who made that sobbing noise which Helen Aylmer believed to be the penitence of Mr. Griffiths, and *you* thought was the kitchen tap."

"Tell me," I asked Omar another day, "what it was really like at the Zoo."

"Awful!" he said, with a shudder at the mere recollection of it. "I am sure you meant no harm, but it was a great error of judgment on your part. Those twinges of rheumatism which I still get from time to time are undoubtedly the result of the damp straw I was given to sleep on, and very probably my illness last November was not unconnected with it.

"As for Irene—she was a pretty two-year-old bitch but rather common; to put you in the picture, think of her as, say, a cinema usherette. I come, you know, of one of the oldest families of bandersnatches in Mazandaran, so we had few mutual acquaintances. But it was pleasant enough to chat about the old country, which she had left more recently than I had; and I found she had a real love of nature. We talked of the mountain slopes carpeted with wild flowers in the spring; of the hot, damp shores of the Caspian with their rice fields and tea plantations. Above all, we exchanged yarns about our raids on the sturgeon fisheries, and I was only sorry that I hadn't any caviare to offer her; the Zoo rations were simply revolting. If even a half of the exploits that she described to me were true, she must have been a real dare-devil as a girl.

"So the first four days passed pleasantly enough and we had soon established a kind of brother-and-sister relationship (so far as this is possible with someone of quite a different class) which suited me well. I even began to forget this gulf that could have come between us. But suddenly, on the fifth day, everything was changed: she was on heat. Now though I had come to enjoy her company, I must confess that she did not attract me physically; she was, as I have already said, socially impossible, and my family had always been very fastidious in such matters. I now found her perpetual provocative posturings, her simpering manner, but above all the vulgarity of her arch little ways, quite disgusting.

"'Come along, deary, don't you want to be naughty?' If she said that once, she must have said it a hundred times. And then she would rub her body against mine and lick my fur and strike the most wanton attitudes. 'No, I don't,' I replied. 'Be a good girl. Go and lie down and let us talk about old times. Did you ever come across the Khayyams, I wonder? Probably not; they always kept themselves very much to themselves.'

"But Irene wouldn't leave me in peace; I still blush to think of some of the tricks she got up to to provoke me to take her. To make matters worse, our two foul-mouthed keepers spied on us perpetually, relieving their boredom with the exchange of coarse observations on my lack of enthusiasm for Irene. One of them doubted whether I knew the facts of life; the other even went so far as to suggest that I might be a queer. Finally they decided to take the matter into their own hands and bring us together.

"The first I knew of this was when they entered our enclosure dressed like baseball players. One seized Irene, who offered no resistance, and the other made for where I was lying. Poor chap, he hadn't a chance in hell. Ten minutes later, after he had run a mile or more without ever even getting near me, he shouted to his colleague to drop Irene and come to his aid. The enclosure was not big; in the end they caught me and carried me to where Irene was eagerly awaiting my coming. She turned her head and winked at me in a perfectly odious way. I began to feel rather sick.

"The Zoo should issue their keepers with more effective protective clothing. I had already sized the stuff up and had little doubt that I could get my teeth through it; and so it proved. Suddenly I turned round and, summoning all my strength, bit Bert so savagely on the hand that he cried out and let go of me. Then I turned upon Jimmy, and a second later I was free again.

"So that was that! Irene's season was as good as over, and no more attempt was made to coerce the uncoerceable. Her passion cooled, she stopped playing the harlot and became again the good companion that she had been at first. She was a nice girl really, and bore me no grudge. She even tried to blame herself for my failure: 'I wasn't classy enough for you,' she said. 'Perhaps next time they'll give you a real lady.'

"I licked her face and took my leave of her."

It must have been about this time, I think, that news reached England that Pixleigh had found the Abominable Snowman. It would really be more correct to say that the Abominable Snowman had found Pixleigh, and that there was very little left of Pixleigh afterwards.

The party had come across fresh spoors in a high valley of the Kinchinjanga range, near the Kabru. They pitched camp for the night; but at about two o'clock in the morning there was a sudden blood-curdling roar as the Snowman attacked one of the tents—the one in which Pixleigh and his two companions were sleeping.

The night was extremely dark, and though the Sherpas ran out immediately with guns and torches, they were too late to save the three Englishmen, or to revenge their deaths other than by some very wild firing in the direction in which the monster appeared to have vanished. The bodies of Pixleigh's companions were found under the fallen tent, but it was not until daylight came that a few scattered and relatively unimportant fragments of Pixleigh were recovered, at a point about half a mile from the camp. The Sherpas,

disinclined to share the fate of the Englishmen, started back
at once for the base camp, bringing with them the bodies
of Hart and Fergusson (the two other men) and a little
bit of collar-bone to represent Pixleigh.

"Poor Pixleigh!" said Omar. "He always wanted to see
the Himalaya again before he died, and he just managed
it."

Another subject on which I sometimes attempted to draw
Omar was that of his various close relations—the other
members of the family.

"As you probably know," he said, "we came from Africa
originally, and most of our cousins are still there—in various
parts of the continent from Abyssinia to the Cape. In pre-
historic times there were hyraxes—or as some prefer,
hyraces—in Egypt and also in parts of Greece, but nothing
now remains of them beyond a handful of bones. Outside
Africa there are only the Jewish branch of the family—
the 'coney' (Hebrew *shapham*) of the Old Testament—
and ourselves.

"Perhaps the oddest thing about us is that we hyraxes
form a group of such little creatures, whereas our nearest
living relations—the horse, the rhinoceros and the elephant
—are large, or even enormous. Our extinct Greek cousins
were about the size of donkeys, I believe, but they disappeared more than a million years ago.

"Our family is in a glorious muddle, and scientists are
incessantly making the muddle worse by tinkering about
with its nomenclature. They erred at the start by choosing
the name Hyrax, which is the Greek for a shrew-mouse;

we are *not* shrew-mice, and never have been.

"Now *Heterohyrax syriacus,* the Biblical 'coney.' Coney is of course an old English word for a rabbit: rabbits are rodents; the so-called coney is an ungulate. According to *Leviticus* xi, 5 and *Deuteronomy* xiv, 7, the Lord (who, after all, *created* the coney) informed Moses that it chewed the cud but did not divide the hoof; actually it divides the hoof but does not chew the cud, though to the casual observer it may give the impression of doing so. So the Lord condemned the coney as unclean for not being cloven-hoofed; in fact, according to His rules it was unclean for not being a cud-chewer. Really one cannot avoid the conclusion that Moses received only rather general briefing, and with his very imperfect knowledge of zoology made a serious blunder.

"I am more in sympathy with Solomon—or whoever was the author of the Book of Proverbs. Though he had a poor opinion of the coney's physique, he does at least commend his intelligence—along with that of the ant, the locust and the spider (a mixed bag indeed!). 'A feeble folk,' he says of the coney; 'little upon the earth, but . . . exceeding wise.'[2] High praise that, if it came from Solomon (who could converse with animals)."

"You asked me the other day about the food we ate at home," Omar said one evening while we were playing liar dice. "Well—chiefly it was the fresh young tips of leaves or bracken fronds, and any fruit we could get hold of.

[2] Proverbs XXX, 24–6.

Sometimes Father and Mother would 'go shopping' as they called it—which meant going down to Parus and snatching a bunch of grapes or a pomegranate from one of the market stalls. Their consciences were always a little uneasy after such a raid, but they justified the theft on the grounds that it was done 'for the children.' Father and Mother rarely ate stolen fruit themselves.

"We also spent a good deal of time chewing the bark of young trees. This, I now realize, added to our diet the wood alcohol that is so necessary to us, young and old alike; and it explains why, in captivity, bandersnatches often take to the bottle. Bark-chewing was our equivalent both of your sweet-sucking and your drinking, and we do not consider it to be contrary to the precepts of the Prophet. (Incidentally, I sometimes feel heartily ashamed of the fact that I have failed to keep the fast of *Ramadan* since I came to England.) Our lower classes also eat grasshoppers and little moths, but Mother always said it was 'common'—like eating whelks at Blackpool—and told us not to do it. I tried a small green grasshopper once, but did not care for it."

It was talk such as this that helped us to pass the long winter evenings—not indeed that help was needed, for we were blissfully happy together. By day Omar would lend a hand in the house or—weather permitting—in the garden. "That wisteria needs drastic pruning," he announced one afternoon (it hadn't been touched since Father's death); "leave it to me." And with his sharp teeth he shortened the lateral spurs like a real professional, without of course hav-

ing to use a ladder. And sometimes I would take him out
with me in the car.

I taught him to make an omelet, and he soon became quite

a competent cook. He in turn showed me how to prepare
dugh, the popular Persian sour buttermilk, and was very
disappointed when I had to admit that I didn't like it. But
he also made *dushab* for me—a delicious kind of grape
syrup which I could unreservedly praise.

Sometimes he read to me in his small and rather high-
pitched voice. Usually it was a story about animals, and he
was especially fond of the writings of Gerald Durrell, David
Attenborough and Gavin Maxwell. "That man Maxwell," he

said, *"really* loves animals." I got these books for him out of the Dorking Public Library.

But perhaps his greatest pleasure was, and remained, telecolour, and I was astonished by the quickness of his intelligence when there was a thriller. Often he seemed to be barely attending to what was happening on the screen, yet he would suddenly say, "The murderer is that waitress with the false pearl ear-rings. She put rat poison in his Bovril."

"What—that charming girl?—she'd never do a thing like that!" (I was a fool in such matters.)

But he was always right.

Omar was a genius with figures, as I discovered one day quite by chance. I was at my writing-table, trying to work out something about one of my investments, and it was really to myself that I said, "I wish I knew what 4½ per cent of £860.9.6 was!" Omar replied in a flash, "I make it £38.14.15." I thought he was joking, but after ten minutes' hard work I arrived at the same figure.

"How on earth did you do it?" I asked.

"Just multiply by 9 and divide by 200."

"But in *your head?"*

"Well—why not?"

One of our greatest fears was that Omar's new way of life would be discovered by some snooper or chance visitor. At night, of course, we locked doors and drew the curtains carefully, and by day we took all reasonable precautions. Lusty, at this time, was always among the vegetables and never came uninvited up to the house. Only Helen Aylmer ever came through the garden proper, and we could always see her as she crossed the lawn. But the danger remained.

I have, I think, already said that we usually had our evening meal in front of the drawing-room fire. But in order that Omar might practise his table-manners, from time to time we ate in style in the dining-room, Omar sitting on my old high-chair. One evening, just as we had finished one of these formal dinners, the dogs began to bark, and immediately there was a peal on the front door bell and a loud bang on the door. I shut the dining-room door and went into the hall; outside I heard Helen's voice crying, "Quick—Let me in!"

The Rectory was on fire, the telephone out of order. Before I could stop her (and in any case I could not of course have stopped her), Helen had rushed into the dining-room, where she knew our telephone to be. Omar just had time to spring from his chair and hide; but there was the chair itself, the two places laid, the stub of a cigar still smouldering. Distraught though she was, Helen could not have failed to notice all this.

I ran back with her to the Rectory to see if I could be of any help. The drawing-room curtains were ablaze, and Ralph was throwing pails of water rather wildly at the walls— doing, I thought, more harm than good. Five minutes later two fire engines arrived, and in another five minutes all was over but the extensive mopping-up.

Helen thanked me and added, "Don't you bother; you've got a guest. I'm sorry to have taken you away from him."

"Yes—my cousin. She felt unwell and went upstairs to lie down."

"But I thought you hadn't got any relations except your uncle?"

I had blundered. "Well—not really a cousin, but Father always called her Cousin Diana."

"She smokes cigars?"

"Yes. I think perhaps it was the cigar that made her sick."

"Does she always sit in a baby-chair?"

"Ah!—funny you should notice that! I brought it down from the attic to see if it might do for her little boy—such a dear: not yet quite three."

"But it looked as though she'd been sitting in it; it was opposite her plate, wasn't it? And why the tiny spoons and forks?"

"Really, Helen, I don't see why I should be subjected to this catechism. I'd ask you in to meet her, but she's going off early tomorrow morning. Well—now I must be getting back to see if Diana is all right."

It was perfectly clear to me that Helen hadn't believed a word of it. But she hadn't a scrap of imagination, and I was equally certain that she had never for a moment thought of Omar. She would no doubt tell Ralph that I had a dwarf "follower."

One day, to my great surprise, I received a letter from Uncle Robert; he was in England on business and proposed coming down to Disbourne to see me. I offered to put him up, but warned him of the probable discomfort. He replied that he would rather come over to lunch and spend the afternoon with me—which really suited me better.

Uncle Robert arrived in a chauffeur-driven Rolls. He was like Father to look at, but quite unlike him in every other way—a gay, rather flashily-dressed bachelor of about seventy, full of *bonhomie* and *joie de vivre* and wisecracks. Lunch was a success. I can cook rather well when I want to, but normally I don't trouble; however I made an effort on this occasion and Omar made the *dushab*. Uncle Robert was full of praise. As luck would have it, Corton was his favourite burgundy and he drank the best part of a bottle. "Your father," he said, "couldn't tell burgundy from claret, and he would eat any muck that was put before him. I despise a guy who can't enjoy the good things of life."

I was glad that I had bought a bottle of brandy and a couple of decent cigars. By the end of the meal Uncle Robert was in fine form, and it was at this point that I introduced Omar, whom I had persuaded to stay in the kitchen until I called him. Omar behaved admirably, and Uncle Robert pronounced him a "jolly little beast." He said he hoped I was satisfied with his present.

"You simply couldn't have given me anything that would have pleased me more."

"Well," said Uncle Robert, "I'm going to—now!"

Honestly I hadn't the slightest idea what he meant. I had laid myself out to please him because he was, after all, my only living relation, and also because he had given me such a wonderful present—a present so much more wonderful than he knew. He now embarked upon what appeared to be a carefully rehearsed speech:

"Rose, I am a rich man—a very rich man. But so long as my brother was alive, there wasn't a cent coming his way

—or yours. I loathed that guy. He bullied me when I was young and patronized me when I was older. He was a sanctimonious prig; I'm sorry to have to say it, but there it is. Well—I came down here today to have a look at you. I haven't got where I am without learning to sum up people pretty quick. Any woman who has Corton '67 in her cellar and who knows how to choose a cigar is O.K. by me. I admire your courage in wearing shorts; all the women do where I come from. I've made up my mind: you shall get my money when I die—the whole dam' lot. But I ain't going to die yet—not by a long chalk—so here's something to be going on with."

He took out his cheque-book, filled in a cheque, folded it and handed it to me. Almost before I had time to thank him, he had jumped into his car and was speeding down the drive. Then I looked at the cheque: it was for *fifty thousand pounds!*

The first thing I did was to sell the old Rover and buy a brand new Jaguar.

Omar had spoken of our sharing our secret for the rest of the winter, but spring came, and summer, and he continued to refuse to let me confide in Rutherton or anyone else. He was still in the prime of life, I well knew; but there could always be an accident. Also he now chain-smoked and often drank more than was wise—including whisky, which formerly he had so much disliked—and I was far from happy about his general health. Yet our perfect platonic relationship was without a cloud, and I hated the idea of doing anything that might possibly disrupt it.

In any case Rutherton was out of England. He had managed to escape from his coypus, and had been for many months in the Argentine, making a photographic record of the sex-life of the apar, or three-banded armadillo. "And *very* odd it is," he wrote to me from Rosario. "I am doing a kind of Kinsey report, and most of my findings will not be suitable for the general public. But *how is Omar?*" I felt something of a cad when I had to reply that the situation was unchanged: that Omar continued from time to time to utter a word or two, but that I had not been able to persuade him to come out into the open. I don't like having to tell lies, but one is sometimes driven to it.

Then, in September, Rutherton returned to England, and almost the first thing he did was to come over to Disbourne. I was delighted to see him again; he seemed to me to be more handsome than ever, and just as charming. I had implored Omar to let me confide in him, but he would not agree. However, Omar was very amiable, and as he greeted him he said what sounded like, "I've never seen a jaguar . . ."

"What did he say?" said Rutherton.

"Well, it *sounded* like, 'I've never seen a Jaguar'; but heaven knows what that means. He *has* seen a Jaguar: I've just bought one."

"But—*don't you know your Kipling?* 'I've never seen a Jaguar, nor yet an Armadillo . . .' Did you tell Omar that I'd been photographing armadillos?"

"Well, I dare say I did."

Rutherton was in a frenzy of excitement; but Omar immediately dried up and refused to repeat what he had said. He became once again the dumb and unresponsive animal; as he told me later, the temptation to surprise Rutherton had suddenly proved irresistible, but he had immediately regretted his action.

"If only I could have Omar for a month or two, I *know* I could get him to talk," said Rutherton.

Omar gave me a look which said more clearly than words, *"Don't you dare . . . !"* I told Rutherton that it wasn't possible. He took his departure with much reluctance, and I could see that he was in the same state that I had previously been in: he could not decide whether or not our ears had been deceiving us.

It was about a fortnight after Rutherton's visit that I had an idea. Among Father's very few friends was a distinguished scientist named Sir William Danecourt, F.R.S.— in fact a physicist, but very knowledgeable in many fields and a man of undoubted integrity. I decided to try to persuade Omar to talk with him.

At first Omar was unwilling. "How do you know that he is to be trusted?" he asked.

"If he gives me his word, then you can rely on him. Father always spoke of him in the highest terms, though he admitted that he could be intolerably abrupt on occasions."

To my great joy—but very much to my surprise—Omar at last consented. "I admit I don't like it," he said. "It would be so easy for something to go wrong. But *you* want it—and you have done so much for me. Let us go and see him, and as soon as possible."

Sir William lived near Sevenoaks, and that evening I rang him up.

"Sir William," I said, "I have a favour to ask of you. May I come over and see you? It is a matter of some urgency and of the greatest scientific importance. I can't say more on the telephone, but I promise you will not be disappointed."

He was a man of few words: "Lunch tomorrow, one o'clock—and don't be late." And he rang off.

"You had better stay in the car until I've got Sir William's promise," I said to Omar, as we drew up under the portico of his handsome Regency house. "Be good! Here's your lunch."

I rang the front door bell with some trepidation. Sir William was a notorious misogynist, and I had only once been to his house; my role had then been that of chauffeur

to Father, and Sir William had treated me with a brusque-
ness almost indistinguishable from rudeness. It was said
that on more than one occasion female reporters had fled
from his door at the mere sight of his butler, a man of
enormous size and gorilla-like aspect who had been carefully selected as being likely to discourage the curious,
especially those of the fair sex; and any who succeeded in
bypassing the ogre soon fled before his hardly less intimi-
dating master.

Sir William was about seventy-five, of apostolic but un-
couth appearance, a kind of untidy identikit concocted out
of late portraits of Darwin, Tolstoy and Ruskin. We lunched
in silence punctuated only by commonplaces; he obviously
regretted the momentary lapse into good nature that had
landed him in so disagreeable a situation. It was not until
coffee had been brought into the study, and the butler had
left us alone together, that I explained to him why I had
come. Of course he didn't believe a word of it.

"My dear young woman, the age of miracles is past and
I'm far too busy to waste my time on some ventriloquist
hoax."

"It's *not* a hoax, Sir William. If you will give me your
word not to mention Omar's power of speech to anyone
without his consent and mine, then I will bring him in. He
is outside in the car. It will only take five minutes."

He had wasted an hour; what difference did a few more
minutes make? Humour this lunatic and then throw her
out. So, it seemed to me, he was saying to himself. "Very
well, I promise. I will give you *exactly* five minutes—for
your father's sake."

I ought to have remembered that Sir William had a weak heart. When Omar walked in, a few paces ahead of me, and said "Good afternoon, Sir William. It's very kind of you to spare us some of your valuable time . . ." the old man flopped forward in his chair, spilling his coffee all over his trousers and crying out, "My pills! My pills!"

I had to fetch the butler, which was awkward. But Omar remained silent while the pills were being found and administered. "He gets these turns from time to time," said the man. "He'll be all right again in a moment. If not, give him a couple more"; then, as Sir William opened his scared eyes, he withdrew.

"I am indeed sorry, Sir William . . ." Omar began; but I signed to him to be silent, for the old man seemed to be on the point of another collapse. However, he rallied and said, "How is it done? I've never seen anything so convincing."

It was not until he had subjected Omar to a number of tests, searched for concealed wiring, and sent me out into the hall so that he could be alone with him, that he finally said: "Miss Bavistock—are you aware that this is the most significant event in the whole long history of science? I must ring up Lord Hoxton at once."

"You most certainly must not. Remember your promise!"

"But you don't intend, you *can't* intend, to keep this— this amazing thing to yourself? I did not believe you, and in spite of my reputation no one would believe me. There *must* be other witnesses, a full investigation, tape-recordings . . . I *beg* you, Miss Bavistock, in the cause of science,

for the reputation of England, for the sake of civilization . . ."

"Those are big words, Sir William. But the decision rests
with Omar, not with me."

For a couple of hours or more we three argued the
matter, Sir William urging the incredible scientific importance of Omar's achievement while Omar, though obviously flattered, stressed his great dislike of all forms of
publicity. "I am so happy living quietly with Miss Bavistock," he said. "Why must we spoil it all?" but finally
he agreed to the following: that he would appear before
the Fellows of the Royal Society, submit to cross-examina-
tion and allow tape-recordings to be made, provided that
absolute secrecy was guaranteed. Nothing was to be published, no recording re-played other than to Fellows of the
Society, no mention of his gift made to anyone without his
consent. He said that he would like to address the Society,
and he also stipulated that I should accompany him to the
meeting.

As Sir William had foreseen, even his considerable reputation was insufficient to convince the Society that "the talking bandersnatch" was not just a piece of trickery. Five
of the Fellows firmly refused to attend, saying that their
mere presence at the meeting would be enough to damage
their prestige if it even came to be known. They made it
clear that they considered Sir William had been imposed
upon, and it was probably their private opinion that his
fine brain had at last begun to give way. Of the remainder,
Sir William doubted whether a single one had agreed to be
present other than out of loyalty to himself. Had Omar died

at this moment, not a scientist in Europe would have accepted even a sworn statement from Sir William.

Omar had asked whether he might address the Society formally—in other words, deliver a paper. The President, Lord Hoxton, was among the most sceptical of those who had agreed to attend; it seemed to him however that he might as well be hanged for a sheep as for a lamb, and he gave his consent. Moreover since a bandersnatch could not speak, it could hardly deliver an address. In any case the meeting was to be recorded as "Private Business" and not further particularized in the *Transactions*.

One grey November day I drove Omar up to London, reaching Burlington House shortly before three o'clock. I now of course had absolute confidence in Omar, who had given me his assurance that, however much provoked, there would be no repetition of the fiasco at the Telecolour Centre. I wanted his impact on these doubting Thomases to be as sensational as possible; I therefore kept him in the anteroom until the Fellows were seated. Then he entered at my side, bowed to the assembly, and jumped up into his own little chair which I had brought along with us. There was a stir among the audience; though total scepticism still prevailed, it could not be denied that Omar had made a pretty effective entry.

Sir William, introducing the speaker, said that the Royal Society, as everyone knew, had more than three hundred years of glorious history behind it, yet he would venture to predict that today's meeting would go down in its annals as the most momentous ever held. He went on to an admission of his own initial scepticism, and his subsequent conviction that no trickery could possibly have been involved.

"Poor old boy," I heard my neighbour whisper. "It's really rather pathetic. He was brilliant in his day."

After a very generous tribute to my part in the affair, Sir William concluded, "And now, gentlemen, I call upon Mr. Omar to address the Society on"—and he referred to his notes—"'Intercommunication between animals, with special reference to certain members of the Order *Ungulata*'—Mr. Omar!"

Omar rose to his feet amid loud applause, most of which will have been ribald, and with a gesture of his right paw silenced his audience. Then he turned towards Lord Hoxton and said:

"Mr. President; Gentlemen. Let me begin by saying how deeply I appreciate the honour you have done me . . ."

But before he could proceed any further, the whole audience sprang to its feet and broke into a wild cheering which was to sound on the tape-recording like one of the noisier bombardments of the Second World War. Visitors arriving at the Private View of the Royal Academy's Winter Exhibition gazed upwards in astonishment; the police on duty in the forecourt clutched their truncheons more tightly; a pigeon about to alight on one of the Society's window-ledges took off again in fright and did not venture upon another landing until it reached Trafalgar Square. At last the President succeeded in restoring some kind of order, and Omar continued:

"Deeply gratified though I am by your kind and enthusi-

astic welcome, I must beg you to allow me to continue my address without further interruption. For I believe I have things to tell you which are of interest, and may possibly even be of some importance . . ."

I had no idea what Omar was going to say, for he had not taken me into his confidence. He spoke brilliantly,

without a single note, without a hesitation, for an hour
and forty minutes. Though I had often discussed this very
subject with him, much of what he said was quite new
to me, and some of it was far above my head. What I here
give of his address is taken from the text subsequently
printed (from the tape recording) in the *Transactions* of the
Society:

"It has been alleged by your scientists, gentlemen, that
there is an absolute line of demarcation between human
language and the means of communication of all the so-
called 'lower' animals; that the two are not of the same
kind, any more than human society in its variety of organi-
zation is of the same kind with the instinctive herding of
wild cattle or swarming of insects, any more than human
architecture with the instinctive burrowing of the bandersnatch and nest-building of the bird, any more than human
industry and accumulation of capital with the instinctive
hoarding of the bees and beavers. In all these cases, you
say, the action of men is a result of the adaptation of
means at hand to the satisfaction of felt needs, or of purposes dimly perceived at first, but growing clearer with
gradually acquired experience.

"There is just the same *saltus,* you maintain, existent
in the difference between man's conventional speech and
the natural communication of the lower races as in that
between men's forms of society and the instinctive asso-
ciations of the lower races. You say that no addition to or
multiplication of 'brute' speech would make anything like
human speech; that the two are separated by a step which
no animal below man has ever taken. These things, gen-

tlemen, are *lies*—and I am here today as a living refuta-
tion of these lies."

After more in this vein, Omar turned from the general
to the particular, to draw the attention of his audience to
Bandersnatch—a language with a complicated grammar and
syntax and as highly inflected as German. "I have been
working during these last few weeks," he said, "on a little
English-Bandersnatch dictionary and phrase-book. With the
support of Linguaphone records, which I hope also to
make, it should enable any competent linguist to learn to
converse with a Bandersnatch in Hyrcania, a Coney in
Syria or a Dassie in South Africa; for the languages spoken
by these various members of the Procaviidae family differ no
more than does the Arabic of the Egyptian from that of the
Baghdadi. As an Ungulate I can often get the gist of what
is said by an Elephant, whose language is related to ours
much as Dutch is to German, and as it happens I can
speak fairly fluent Horse. Yet of the speech of the Marmot—an animal which superficially I quite closely resemble
—I can understand hardly a single word, the Rodent group
of languages being as remote from ours as is the Slavonic
from the Romance."

Birdsong, said Omar, also presented formidable difficulties to a mammal, though in his time he had given it some
attention. When in Mazandaran he had struck up an ac-
quaintance with a young *bulbul,* or Persian Nightingale, but
he did not feel that he had mastered more than a smattering
of his song—and even here there was some guesswork involved.

These are but a few of the matters which Omar raised

and discussed with equal brilliance; for the address in its
entirety I must again refer my readers to the *Transactions*
of the Society. Omar perorated as follows:

"Well, gentlemen, my time is nearly up. There is more,
much more, that I would gladly have told you of my experiences in connection with the study of languages. There
is, for example, the question of reading and writing. My
mother could read Persian, but she could not write it. With
infinite patience my kind friend and patroness, Miss Bavistock, has taught me to write the Latin alphabet; but I may
well be the only 'animal' who has as yet mastered the art
of committing words to paper. However, this is only the
beginning. The day may not be far distant when these
barriers between man and animal shall have been broken
down, though doubtless we shall have to fight, as the
coloured races are still having to fight, for proper recognition. Yet in England many an animal is already more
fortunately placed than is the Negro immigrant. Dogs and
Cats are given the freedom of the house and may go almost anywhere with their owners except to church. They
sleep on—or even in—their owners' beds, where few if any
Negroes would find a welcome. Horses and greyhounds
fetch sums undreamed of even by those slave-traders who
trafficked in Circassian virgins. Many a young girl, if forced
to choose between her sister and her favourite Pony, would
not hesitate to sacrifice the former.

"Who, fifty years ago, would have dared to predict the
mammoth strides that science has since made? Yes, the
time may come—and sooner than some of us imagine—
when the Primate is a non-human, and the Prime Minister
—who knows?—a Bandersnatch."

I thought the cheering would never stop. Then these famous men, with their beards and doctorates and peerages, began to behave like schoolboys on the end-of-term train. They jumped on the chairs, upset the inkpots, hugged one another like footballers after the scoring of the winning goal. Lord Hoxton, who looked a hundred plus, swung backwards and forwards on the chandelier until they came crashing together to the ground. I *think* Sir Hans d'Aubeny made me an offer of marriage, but such was the uproar that I cannot be sure.

And they were hugging Omar too—till he managed to break away and take refuge up on the cornice. I could see that he was exhausted, and I implored Sir William to help me get him out of the room; but Sir William was himself trying to reach the door to telephone for an ambulance for Lord Hoxton. It was the best part of forty minutes before, more dead than alive, we finally made our escape.

Among the five Fellows who had refused to attend the special meeting was Professor Isaiah Casteels, probably the most distinguished living zoologist; he was no friend of Sir William, who told me that his refusal had been couched in the most offensive language. It must therefore have been particularly galling for Casteels when he discovered that it was the unanimous verdict of those present that Omar was *not* a hoax, and that he had missed the most remarkable address ever given to the Society. Two days later, as Omar and I were washing up after lunch, I heard a car coming up the drive; then the bell rang, and I found Professor Casteels on my doorstep, demanding to see Omar. I recognized him at once by his famous red beard.

I decided that I would teach him a lesson. I said that Omar had agreed to appear before the Royal Society, that he had duly done so, and that for the present he was giving no more interviews.

"Are you aware who I am?" said the Professor, trying to edge his way through the door.

"Certainly: your beard is unmistakable. You are one of the five doubting Thomases, one of those five Foolish Virgins who had the chance and didn't take it. Now you're too late."

"I must insist. I enter in the name of Science." And he pushed past me into the hall.

"Very well; then you will exit in the name of Safety. Omar, show this gentleman out!"

Omar had of course overheard all that we had been saying. In a flash he had his teeth into the Professor's calves and had torn his trouser-legs into shreds. Then—and it was an inspired afterthought—he *prestissimo*'d into the drive and neatly punctured the two front tyres of his car.

Alas it was a Pyrrhic victory! Casteels was undoubtedly a fine zoologist, but he was also a cad; infuriated by the rebuff he had received, he determined upon revenge. Now all those Fellows who had been present at the meeting had been sworn to secrecy: nothing that took place at it was to be mentioned to anyone outside the Society. Casteels, since he had not been present, had not taken this pledge; yet as a Fellow he had been given by some of

the other Fellows, and in all good faith, an exact account
of what had occurred. He decided to inform the Press.

You can imagine my horror and disgust, and Omar's
righteous indignation, when a few days later I opened *The
Times* and found on its centre page:

A TALKING BANDERSNATCH

Professor Isaiah Casteels, the distinguished zoologist, here
describes what may well be the most sensational event of
the century . . . imagination boggles . . . so the age of
miracles is not past . . . staggering . . . almost unbelievable . . .

There followed a pretty accurate account of what had taken
place. The matter was further discussed in a fourth leader,
whose author remained, however, sceptical. He said that
at the moment the story was without corroboration. Professor Casteels had an international reputation as a zoologist, but had he perhaps also a distorted sense of humour?
Had he not been pulling the leg of the Press? "Let us
wait," he concluded, "for the verdict of the President and
those other Fellows of the Society who were also present,
before passing judgment."

He did not have to wait long. The indignation of the
Society at Casteels' treachery knew no bounds. An emergency meeting was called for the same afternoon, at which
Casteels, who was summoned to attend, was forced to ten-
der his resignation. The Fellows then drew up a statement
for the Press, which appeared the following morning in all
the national newspapers:

The President and Fellows of the Royal Society declare
unanimously that they dissociate themselves from the statement made by Professor Isaiah Casteels concerning a meeting
held at the Society's rooms in Burlington House on November
5th last. Professor Casteels was not even present at that meeting, and he has now ceased to be a Fellow of the Society.

It was subscribed by the President (still in hospital but
consulted by telephone) and all the Fellows, including the
other four who had not been present.

Meanwhile Omar and I had been passing the most
wretched twenty-four hours of our lives, expecting every
moment to be invaded by the Press. But here we were
fortunate: for some reason or other (though doubtless not
out of decency) Casteels had not mentioned my name,
and by the time that the London reporters had begun to
pester him about the whereabouts of the famous bandersnatch, Casteels had been so thoroughly scared by Lord
Hoxton and some of the other Fellows that he refused to
see them.

Then came the Society's *démenti*. It was supported in
every newspaper by a vigorous attack on Casteels: "To
compare his sense of humour with that of a schoolboy
would be an insult to the latter." "Long contact with
chimpanzees has left its mark upon him." "Irresponsibility
which disgraces British Science." "Has made us a laughing-
stock throughout the civilized world." "The silliest leg-pull
of all time." "The Society did the right thing, the only
possible thing, in expelling him from their number," and
so on. Casteels was horrified when this boomerang struck

him. It seemed to him monstrous that he should be denounced as a liar when he was speaking the truth, even
though this very truth had been previously denounced
by him as a lie. He panicked. Cutting off his red beard,
he left his house by the back door and caught the night
plane to Rome.

For several more weeks the papers continued to feature
and discuss the Talking Bandersnatch, and not unnaturally
the story of Omar's regrettable telecolour appearance was
revived. Might not this be the same animal? Might not the
Royal Society be covering up some further discreditable
episode? A number of fishy characters, believed to be connected with the Press, began to be much in evidence in
Disbourne, and several self-confessed reporters came to my
door.

   I thought it best to see them and tell them a flat lie. I
showed them Omar. I admitted that he had once or twice
uttered sounds which appeared to resemble words, but that
this had never been repeated. I said that Professor Casteels'
story had been a complete fabrication, as the Royal Society
had already stated. I told them they were more than welcome
to photograph Omar if they wished; indeed, I pretended to
be eager that they should do so. But my story seemed to
convince them that they were on the wrong track, and they
declined. They asked me if I knew of any other bandersnatches in England, and I told them that I did not. "But
doubtless there are many more," I added. "The bandersnatch
is not uncommon in captivity and makes a very nice pet. I
got Omar from a London dealer."

After the last one had gone I said to Omar, "I think I fooled them nicely, don't you?"

"All but one," said Omar; "that chap from the *Sunday Gossip*. I don't trust him an inch."

And how right he was! It must have been on the following Tuesday, while we were having tea with the Aylmers, that this man broke into my house and concealed microphones and cameras, worked by remote control, in the drawing-room and dining-room. We suspected nothing, we knew nothing until that awful Sunday when the whole story was blazed across the front page of the *Sunday Gossip,* and it was Mrs. Dudge, overjoyed to find herself the bearer of ill-tidings, who burst in upon us before breakfast with a copy of it in her hands.

I was described as having given an exclusive interview and as having allowed the photographs to be taken. There were pictures of Omar, wine-glass in hand, sitting opposite me at dinner, and of Omar in the drawing-room doing *The Times* crossword (which, incidentally, never took him more than three or four minutes). There was a long and purely fictitious interview in which I was alleged to have described Omar's great talent, my desire to keep the matter secret, and my final resolve that the world should be told, through its leading Sunday newspaper, of this universe-shattering event.

"Well," said Mrs. Dudge. "Is it true, or isn't it?"

"Whatever it is," I replied, "it's no business of yours. Kindly get out of my house!"

Part IV
VICIT

I

"Birds, beasts and fishes, are so learned grown,
They speak the English language as their own."
Madame Grimalkin's Party, 1808

"There is only one thing to do," I said to Omar. "We must leave this house immediately."

Hastily I packed a few necessities for us both and crammed them and the two dogs into the Jaguar. In the drive we almost collided with a carload of reporters; they turned and tried to follow us, but the Jaguar was too quick for them and they soon lost track of us.

I had no idea what we were going to do or where we were going to go; I simply knew that we must get away from Disbourne. After about ten miles we took a little side-road and stopped to take stock of the situation. Then Omar had an inspiration: "Let's go to Sir William," he said. "He got us into this fix (though it really wasn't his fault); he must get us out of it. I believe him to be a man of honour. He has a large and comfortable house. He can't very well refuse to take us in."

The butler scowled when he saw us, but Sir William was perfectly splendid; he did not even raise any objection to the dogs. He was, of course, delighted to have the "guinea-pig" under his roof; but it was for the sake of the honour of the Royal Society that he welcomed us so warmly. "That bounder Casteels," he said. "If he sets foot in this country again I'll shoot him. He has disgraced the Society. You are all my guests so long as you care to stay."

There was of course a hue and cry after us all over the country. TALKING BANDERSNATCH VANISHES, and similar headlines, captured the front page of every newspaper; but nobody thought of looking for us at Sir William's. My house (I learned later) was broken into by the Press, but as good luck would have it I had taken the precaution of carrying Omar's autobiographical sketch away with me, and they did not find anything else that they could make use of. Lord Hoxton was also pestered by reporters; but he was well able to look after himself, and sent them packing. Meanwhile Omar and I remained with Sir William—still made welcome, but still uncertain what course of action to pursue.

But one evening after dinner Omar said, much to my astonishment, "Sir William, I have come to a decision—and it is one that will I think both surprise and please you: I am coming out into the open. I feel it is my duty in the interests of science, and for the sake of my fellow 'animals' whose conditions I might be able to improve. You may do what you like with me, and I promise to collaborate. I think it might be best if I addressed the nation on telecolour; would you be able to arrange it? You must remember that I have already blotted my copy book with the BBC, and they may raise objections. But probably you would be able to fix it."

Sir William was delighted: it would be fame indeed for him if this great event were to take place under his aegis. Next morning he went up to London to see Lord Glossop at Broadcasting House; and though Lord Glossop was at first sceptical, believing the whole thing to be a newspaper racket, Sir William succeeded at last in convincing him. On January 23rd Omar, with Rutherton as telecolourcaster, was telecoloured to the nation.

Omar talked for twenty minutes. He spoke gaily, touching on his early life, his capture, and the kindness he had received in England—and here he generously mentioned me by name. "There is probably no other country in the world," he said, "where 'animals' are in general more humanely treated. Yet much still remains to be done." He went on to consider the plight of old horses, of unwanted cats, of over-pampered dogs killed by kindness. "But people sometimes talk of cattle brutally herded together in railway trucks. I once travelled on the Underground in the rush hour, and I would gladly have changed places with them." He praised the spirit of the RSPCA, though not always its actions, and the admirable work being carried out by UFAW. "I intend," he concluded, "to use the talents that God has given me to improve the lot of every 'animal' in England; and if, as I very much hope, I may be allowed to play some small part in the life of this country, I shall do so to the very best of my ability. God bless England! God save the Queen! Goodnight—and thank you for listening to me."

After the programme we were conducted by Lord Glossop to his office for a drink. Omar and Sir William were soon deep in learned discussion on the subject of frogs, and I heard Omar say, "But surely, Sir William, as every school-boy knows, the omosternum is simply a median ossification on the coracoscapular process of the batrachian. . . ." Lord Glossop and I sat back and listened in wondering silence.

An hour later Omar was placed in an empty crate labelled RARE OLD JAMAICA RUM and smuggled out of a back en-trance of the building to Sir William's waiting car. There we rejoined him and were driven back to his house.

Once again the Press was baffled.

It so happened that on the day of this memorable event the Labour Government, which had almost reached the end of its term of office, was unexpectedly defeated in the House, and a child was born to a Russian astronautess in a space station. Under normal circumstances, one or other of these "sensations" would certainly have captured the headlines in the morning papers; in fact they were both tucked away in a corner, along with the daily progress-report on the Chipping Sodbury sextuplets. Omar's achieve-ment was spread across all the main news-pages. Even *The Times* went quite berserk, and the *Daily Telegraph* printed the whole of its front page in vermilion.

The universe gasped; only Russia doubted. Yet the doubt-ing Russian scientists were divided among themselves. Prochnikoff, their most famous zoologist, stated that the whole thing was a fraud: animals never had, and never could, speak rationally. He challenged Omar to come to Moscow. His great rival, Uchinsky, on the other hand, maintained that this was nothing new. There had been a Russian bear who knew the works of Pushkin by heart and had made recordings of some of his finest poems; admittedly the animal was now dead, but the recordings remained. Russia had, as always, been first in the field. Yet a third scientist, Metchnikoff, weighed in. Northern Hyrcania, he said, had formerly been a part of the USSR, and though the British alleged that Omar had been kidnapped in the southern (or Persian) part of the country, this was not to be credited. Omar's parents were undoubtedly Russian by birth, therefore Omar was Russian also. The civilized world ignored these interruptions.

Sir William was in a state of perpetual ecstasy. When I was alone with him he said: "That an animal should be able to speak *with meaning* is marvel enough. Were Omar able to say no more than 'The cat is on the mat,' *understanding what 'cat' and 'mat' mean,* this would be a major break-through in the relationship between man and the non-human animal. But I believe Omar to have a brain without its equal in this or in any other age. He has proved that it is *man* who is the inferior animal. I have, as you know, been having long sessions with him, and I say this advisedly: in his presence I feel myself entirely second-rate. This is the most astonishing scientific event in the whole history of our civilization; I am old now, and like Joseph I am ready to sing my *Nunc Dimittis*."

"Surely Simeon, Sir William," said Omar, who came into the room at that moment.

"Simeon, of course. I stand corrected."

From now on, Omar and I were to lead a completely new existence. Sir William had been in touch with the Chief of the Metropolitan Police, who was an old friend of his, and through his good offices it was arranged that when we returned to Disbourne we should be afforded adequate protection. Two days after the telecolour broadcast we left Sir William's hospitable house and drove home with a police escort. We had become VIPs.

It was now, too, that Uncle Robert's cheque proved invaluable, for it was obviously necessary for us to have a *pied-à-terre* in London. I was fortunate enough to get chambers in Albany. I also needed a secretary, and it suddenly occurred to me that Rutherton might like the job. He had quite forgiven me for the deception I had been obliged to use with him, and I for my part was glad to have this opportunity of making amends for all the trouble we had caused him. Omar gave his approval, and Rutherton became the third member of our team—Omar acting as a kind of chaperon. Incidentally, Uncle Robert wrote me a splendid letter, saying that he was proud to have been the donor of this amazing animal. Business made it impossible for him to leave Canada at the moment, but he fully intended coming as soon as he could to "have a yarn with my famous great-nephew." He added that if I needed any more money he would cable "a hundred thousand bucks or more" at any time. I told him that for the present I had all I needed, and sent him a specially autographed photograph of Omar.

We generally spent the week in London and only week-ends at Disbourne. Rutherton had his own flat in St. John's Wood, but he usually came down with Omar and myself to the country on Friday nights. This reminds me that I have done no more than make casual mention of my invaluable delinquent garden-boy, Lusty; his services deserve better recognition. It was he who now kept an eye on my dogs during the week, feeding and exercising them. I owe him a considerable debt of gratitude.

When Lusty—the son of a local farmer—came out of Borstal, nobody in the village would have anything to do with him. But I had always had a soft spot for him: he was, I thought, an animal who presented a challenge. I decided to try to tame him.

When I engaged him, Father was still alive and very much against the experiment. "You know his record?" he said.

"Of course I know it. Who doesn't? It's been in all the papers. Do you imagine he'll try to rape *me?*"

"I would consider that highly improbable," said Father, rudely. "But anyhow he's a thief. He might steal my books" —which was all Father cared about.

However, I insisted; and I never had occasion to regret it. When I was away Lusty had the keys of the house, yet he never stole a single thing from me. He adored animals and became a great ally of Omar's. As for me, I must confess that I enjoyed seeing this Adonis about the place (though there was a spotty period); even Rutherton was not unmoved. I can't imagine why I haven't mentioned all this earlier; but the book has just grown, and I gave too little thought to the planning of it.

Life in London was terribly hectic. Omar, having decided to place himself at the disposal of his adopted country, was in perpetual demand, and Rutherton and I had to battle ceaselessly to prevent him from overtiring himself. He was badgered to speak at innumerable meetings, to open bazaars, to broadcast, to subscribe to a thousand societies for the welfare of animals, to help lame dogs—both two-legged and four-legged—over stiles, and to dine with *divorcées* duchesses: not a tenth of these invitations was it possible, or indeed desirable, for him to accept.

Down at Disbourne he had originally gone everywhere on all fours; but he now considered this undignified, and in London it would of course have been quite impossible in any case. But he could only walk very slowly on his hind legs, and with a kind of penguin-waddle which he knew to look rather absurd. Sometimes he sat on my shoulder, but this exposed him everywhere to undesirable publicity. Also, thanks to too much good living and—as I thought—too much drinking, he had put on weight. Naturally we went almost everywhere by car; but (as any lame person knows) there still remains, in London, a great deal of walking to be done. In the end I bought one of those two-handed baby-carriers, which Rutherton and I carried between us; it wasn't a perfect solution, but I couldn't think of anything better.

One day we lunched at Buckingham Palace, where the

Queen graciously showed us round the Picture Gallery.
Omar happened to mention to Prince Philip that he could
do the hundred yards in under five seconds, and after
luncheon the Prince took him out into the gardens and
timed him with a stop-watch.

"I make it 5.1 seconds," he said.

"But remember, Sir, it was after your excellent luncheon!"

There was also a supper party with the Prime Minister

and Mrs. Wontson at Number Ten, so that Omar might meet the newly appointed Minister of Livestock. Mrs. Wontson had cooked the meal herself, and Omar was full of praise for her cabbage soup which—to tell the truth—Rutherton and I found rather insipid.

One of the most moving experiences at this time was the occasion when Omar visited the Hostel for Retired Horses at Cricklewood. It was characteristic of him to spare time to bring a ray of sunshine into the twilight lives of these pathetic old hacks, who had been saved from the knackers by the generosity of a handful of local ladies. Omar addressed the assembled animals in Horse, apologizing for his imperfect command of the language; his quip, "horse sense is the sense that horses have that prevents them betting on men," was greeted with frenzied whinnyings by his delighted audience. Then he visited the sick-bay, cheering the many invalids (there had been an epidemic of coughing) by his mere presence and leaving a little bag of oats and a sprig of horse-chestnut in each stall.

It was this visit to Cricklewood, which received a good deal of publicity in the Press, that led to Omar arranging for the making of the famous Linguaphone records, "Horse for Beginners" and "Stable Horse," and composing the booklet *Straight from the Horse's Mouth* which complemented them.

Omar had disclosed, in an interview, that horses had a language which they used when alone together but rarely employed in the presence of humans. Neighing and whinnying were no more than the equivalent of cheering and clapping. Horse, though a very elementary language compared with Bandersnatch, was more than adequate for all that one horse had need of in communicating with another; anyone with a gift for languages could easily learn, in a week or two, enough Horse to get by with. "I would be only too ready," he said, "to make the necessary material available."

Omar, when he made this offer, had probably not foreseen that the demand for him to implement it would come principally from hunting men and women and race-horse owners and trainers. But on reflection he decided that nothing but good would come of it if the horse could make his wants understood by man. Very conscious of the inadequacy of his own Horse, he engaged the services of an intelligent, golden-voiced young filly called Aubergine. The standard phonetic alphabet being insufficient for the purpose, it was agreed that Aubergine, under his direction, should make two records—the first, "Horse for Beginners," giving a selection of useful phrases of a general nature, while the second, "Stable Horse" would provide a kind of equivalent of, say, kitchen Italian.

The sales of the records and booklet brought Omar and his collaborator a small fortune, but they were also to be the cause of a good deal of worry to him. For it soon became apparent that those whose lives revolved round the horse were often in other respects quite uneducated, and in general very poor linguists. This led to many complaints being received. For example, a certain Master of Foxhounds intended to say to his mare, "Go out and graze, but be sure to be back here by two o'clock sharp"; but so defective was his pronunciation that the mare understood him to say, "Go off to Towcester and don't come back before Friday." These difficulties were ultimately overcome by the appointment of resident linguists who acted as interpreters.

A number of race-horse owners arranged for concealed microphones to be installed in their stables, and this brought about the discovery of a lot of hitherto quite unsuspected corruption among horses. To take but one case: Lord Bristowe's interpreter overheard Arpeggio say to Smoker's Cough, the favourite for the National, "I've got a 'grand' on Wisteria; go slow on Saturday and I'll make it worth your while."

However, taken all in all, Omar's project to bring man

and horse closer together proved a valuable contribution to the case of animal welfare. Had time and circumstances permitted, it is probable that he would have attempted something similar for the dog and the cat and so earned the gratitude of three-quarters of the human race.

It was only natural that I should ask Omar what he felt about the keeping of animals in captivity. "Are zoos cruel?" I said. I found myself awaiting his opinion on such occasions as eagerly as Boswell must have awaited Dr. Johnson's or Eckermann that of the aged Goethe.

"This is a matter of the greatest interest and importance," he replied, "and one on which I am well qualified to express views. Let us see what case the supporters of zoos can make. All an animal needs, they say, is food, shelter, companionship, and the opportunity to breed; these a good zoo normally provides. In the wild, an animal has perpetually to fight for survival. It must fight its natural enemies; it must fight to get food for itself and its young. It has to face flood, famine, drought, disease. Animals in captivity live well, look well, and generally breed well. Their life-span is often two or three times what it would be in the wild. Unhappy animals die; therefore animals behind bars must be happy. Such is their argument.

"Now supposing you were to take a young man and his wife and enclose them for life in a small country house surrounded by a high stockade. Give them food and warmth, books and visitors, telecolour and daily papers, careful medical supervision—everything except their liberty. What would happen? While men and women living 'in the wild' were being killed on the roads or in the air, sent to lose limbs or even life in incomprehensible wars, driven to alcohol or ulcers or suicide by overwork or financial worry, poisoned by diesel fumes or worn out by the miseries and exhaustions of commuting, hounded to death by the pitiless tempo of the rat-race—while such horrors were overwhelming those outside the stockade, our happy couple would live on and on, little more confined than a ship's purser yet spared the discomforts of an unstable ocean. Their house would not become too small for them as their family increased, because their children, as soon as they reached the age of irritation, would be packed up in small crates and sold to similar establishments up and down the country. In short, the perfect life. Yet might they not feel that they were missing something?

"The standard answer to the charge that animals miss the pleasures of freedom is that this criticism is the result of muddled thinking based upon emotionalism and an anthropomorphic approach: 'because man would miss his freedom, it does not follow that an animal would miss his.' There is a dangerous grain of truth in this, and it must be admitted that some animals are more affected by captivity than others.

"Take Irene, for example. A very silly girl with an almost non-existent IQ, she is not unhappy as she is; given a highly-sexed mate she would be contented enough. Yet even she—and she told me so herself—often thinks with nostalgia of the old days in Hyrcania. She knows that something is lacking in her life. Even an animal born in captivity must have vague, instinctive yearnings for the life it has never known.

"Another point. It is alleged that man is saving rare animals from total extinction by keeping them in zoos. But why are these animals dying out? Simply because *man* is killing them for their pelts or their tusks or their territory— or just for the sheer fun of it. Here I must pause to praise the fine work being done by those who are establishing nature reserves; but it has been left too late.

"You do not mention the circus—very probably because you can guess my views on the subject already. I had a long and interesting talk in the Cricklewood sick-bay with a superannuated circus horse. He told me that in general there was little cruelty in the training, though he mentioned one or two horrible cases that had come his way. What animals really object to, he said, was the degradation of performing imbecile antics in ridiculous dress before a half-witted audience. The children who came to watch knew no better, and he blamed the parents who brought them; it was as reprehensible as giving them cigarettes or purple hearts. But he could not find adequate words—for Horse is not a rich language—to express the contempt that he felt for those adults who attended circuses on their own.

"So long as zoos exist," Omar said, "I consider that people who want to learn more about animals may reasonably visit them; but the circus should be abolished at once. I hope, however, the time will come when such a mutual understanding is established between man and 'wild animals' that zoos will no longer be necessary: a time when children will feed tigers in Trafalgar Square as fearlessly as they now feed pigeons; a time when one's neighbour in the Underground may be a well-spoken orang-utan, and the traffic warden who fines one for a parking offence a giant panda."

Omar was sensitive about his appearance (I think I have already mentioned how he bulged fore and aft when he stood), and more than once told me how he envied the slender elegance of animals such as the whippet, the gazelle, and some of the cat tribe. But when the *Moon* referred to his "cabriole legs, like those of an imitation Chippendale chair"—incidentally a most inaccurate comparison—he sued the paper. He conducted his own case and was awarded substantial damages—at the moment I forget the exact sum.

He never liked being photographed, but he was of course incessantly pursued by photographers, both professional and amateur; it was one of the penalties of fame. In the autumn he was obliged to give sittings for the illustrations to some of the innumerable books about him which were being prepared for the Christmas market. There were artists and draughtsmen too, but Omar would rarely consent to pose for more than a few minutes. Picasso, wearing his hundred odd years lightly enough, came hopefully from the south of France, but Omar refused even to see him: "I can paint better than that myself," he said. "If old Watts were still alive it would have been a different matter. I would have posed for him."

Omar readily co-operated with the Royal Society and submitted to various tests and experiments. The Society established that his IQ was greater than that of the President
and considerably in excess of that of any of the other
Fellows. He performed a number of calculations at lightning
speed, but was always beaten by the computer. His memory was prodigious: given a copy of *Paradise Lost,* he read
through the first book once and then repeated it by heart
without a single mistake. One day, in a sand quarry near
Disbourne, he demonstrated the manner in which a bandersnatch constructs his burrow. "It was rather undignified," he
said to me afterwards, "but one must be prepared to make
sacrifices in the cause of science."

Rutherton and I were always present at Omar's sessions
with the Royal Society; these were quite informal, any
Fellow raising a point of interest and Omar answering to
the best of his ability. But sometimes of an evening, after
Rutherton had left, Omar and I would go round to Lord
and Lady Hoxton, who also had chambers in Albany.
"Hoxton's port," Omar observed, "is excellent; it almost com-
pensates for Lady Hoxton's conversation."

Lord Hoxton was particularly interested in Irene who—
and I was very surprised to learn this—was at the moment
the only bandersnatch in any of the world's zoos. Since the
Hyrcanian government had now strictly forbidden the ex-
port of bandersnatches (refusing the most tempting offers),
Irene assumed a new importance. Could she be taught to
speak English, Lord Hoxton asked. But Omar was obliged

to reply this was quite out of the question: Irene was a peasant girl who had not properly mastered her own language. She did not know a single word of Persian.

One evening, when Lady Hoxton had left the room to make the coffee, Lord Hoxton said, "Omar, I hardly know how to put this to you, because one has no right to attempt to influence the sex life of one's friends, but—would you not consent to mate with Irene? One of your children might very well inherit your talents. The world would be immeasurably the poorer if this astonishing gift of yours was lost for ever."

But Omar was adamant. "Would you," he said to Lord Hoxton, "be willing to go to bed with a cinema usherette?"

"Well—it would all depend . . ."

Irene, by the way, had—thanks to Omar's fame—become a nine-days' wonder at the Zoo. The bars of her cage were now painted gold, and the Hyrcanian flag flown above it. Thousands of visitors, unable to see Omar in person, flocked to the next best thing, bringing caviare from Fortnum's and bunches of flowers. She simply adored the publicity, making eyes at every male under the age of seventy and waggling her bottom seductively.

One evening, after closing time, Omar went to see her—at his own suggestion. I think myself that this was a mistake, or at all events a mistiming, though he was actuated by the highest motives; for Irene, who was unfortunately on heat, immediately attempted to seduce him. He stayed only a few minutes, and the experiment was never repeated. But Omar was glad that he had been the indirect cause of bringing pleasure and improved conditions to Irene. "Though it was not my fault," he said, "I have always felt that she had rather a rough deal."

About this time there occurred a very important event: the passing of an Act of Parliament by which Omar was made Honorary Human Extraordinary, thus entitling him to all the benefits and all the disadvantages of *homo sapiens*. Soon after, I was given a Life Peerage and took the title of Baroness Bandersnatch of Disbourne, in the county of Surrey.

I asked Omar what he felt about his new honour.

"Well," he answered, "there are certain obvious advantages. Now at last I can visit Westminster Abbey—perhaps even be buried there. I can vote, open a bank account, and use the public lavatory instead of the lamp-post. I could become an MP. I could represent England in the Olympic Games, and since I can do the hundred yards in 4.8 seconds I could hardly fail to win a gold medal or two. I could buy a washing machine on the never-never, or enter my son for Eton. There is, however, the debit side. I shall have to pay income tax at sixteen shillings in the pound, and £3 a week National Health Insurance. I shall be sent to Borstal if I bite a policeman. We will have to see how it all works out."

I must here mention a curious situation which soon arose —one which no one had foreseen. Omar was now human, but he remained naked; technically, therefore, he was liable to instant arrest whenever he appeared in a public place. Most people were ready to accept this anomaly, but two groups of citizens—the Nudists' League and the Society for

the Prevention of Indecency in Animals (the SPIA)—rose in
revolt.

For the Nudists it provided a heaven-sent opportunity for
propaganda. Men and women began to appear stark naked
in various parts of London—Trafalgar Square in particular;
the Labour MP for South-West Reading, where the League
had its headquarters, stripped in the House; and in the
National Gallery a whole family of Nudists were found posing,
in the appropriate postures, in front of Bronzino's allegory,
"Venus, Cupid, Folly and Time." All these people, when
arrested, made the same defence: "If Omar, then why not
us?" At first they were fined; then, when fines had no effect,
prison sentences were imposed. But it remained for that great
spoilsport, the British weather, to give the *coup-de-grâce*
and bring the Nudists back to their senses and their clothes.

The SPIA attacked from quite a different angle, and a
"Pants for Omar" campaign was launched throughout the
length and breadth of the country. By every post Omar
received parcels containing garments ranging from complete
outfits to plastic fig-leaves and *cache-sexe* knitted lovingly
in magenta wool. In the end—and rather cleverly, I thought
—I made arrangements with the Post Office to redirect to the
Nudists' headquarters in Reading all parcels appearing to
contain clothes, thus killing two birds with one stone.

There is another matter, before I forget. One of the
curious by-products, as it were, of Omar's sudden leap to
fame was the immediate popularity of "Omar" and "Bandersnatch" as names for every kind of purpose. Turn on
the wireless, and sooner or later you were subjected to
"The Bandersnatchers"—yet another of those innumerable

quartets of delinquents who have caterwauled their way
into notoriety and who earn more money in a week than
the Prime Minister does in a year. Turn on ICV and you
were urged to buy Bandersnatch butter (almost indistinguishable from margarine), or to get "Omar whiteness and
brightness" into your wash by using Bandersnatch detergent
(with free plastic bandersnatch for the kiddies). Turn to
your crossword, and ten to one you found a four-letter
clue: "Famous animal," or a five-letter clue: "Word once
uttered by famous animal." Every other infant hugged a
talking Teddy Bandersnatch called Omar; every other pros-
titute wore an imitation bandersnatch fur coat. Five new
public houses in England were named the Bandersnatch,
and an Omar Resturant, with *homard à l'Omar* as its
specialité de la maison, opened in Soho. Even the sales of
Omar Khayyam's *Rubaiyat* rose sharply. Oddest of all, perhaps, was the popularity of Omar as a boy's Christian name;
within a year it had edged its way into the "top ten" list
which appears in *The Times* each January.

There were Omar clubs everywhere up and down the
country, whose members greeted one another with a "Cheeri-
omar!" when they met. An Omar stamp was designed, and
a plastic threepenny-bit with the Queen's head on the
obverse and a bandersnatch on the reverse—as though
they formed a kind of duumvirate who governed England.
Then there were Omar's own achievements in the world
of the arts. Twenty-eight thousand reproductions of "Frumious Bandersnatch" were sold, and the long-playing record
of his more important speeches soon beat the record set up
by Churchill's wartime speeches many years back. Never in

the whole history of mankind, had such popularity been achieved before.

I can hardly bring myself to relate the tragic events which now follow, but I will do my best. It is the historian's duty to conceal nothing, however painful.

In spite of the innumerable calls made upon his time, Omar had managed to keep up his painting; like Sir Winston Churchill, he found in it the perfect relaxation. When the Tryout Galleries proposed holding a one-man show of his work, both painting and sculpture, he was at first diffident; "After all," he said, "I am only an amateur." But finally, though very reluctantly, he agreed. The Private View was fixed for December 10th, and invitations to it were in tremendous demand.

At the beginning of December Omar was far from well. I could see that he was tired and often sleepy, and he was eating almost nothing. Then he began to complain of breathlessness. He coughed a great deal, and I noticed that he frequently clutched his chest; but when I urged him to see a doctor he said, "It's nothing. And in any case I'm far too busy." He had insisted upon supervising the hanging of his pictures, and on the eve of the Private View he decided to go round again to the Gallery after dinner to cast a final eye on the arrangement. I saw how exhausted he was, and begged him to stay at home; but once he had made up his mind to do anything it was useless to try to stop him. I rang up the Bosomstones, who run the Gallery, and they picked us up in their car.

Omar was always meticulous about the hanging of a

picture. Bosomstone was made to lower this one, to heighten that; to space these more closely, those farther apart. Omar, his third large whisky-and-soda beside him and a Tom Thumb cigar in his mouth, had found a comfortable seat upon the summit of his most important piece of sculpture, "Bandersnatch Warren"—the product of a prolonged study of the structure of Gruyère cheese; from this vantage-

point he directed operations, perpetually urging poor Bosomstone up and down the rickety stepladder which fat Mrs.
Bosomstone attempted to steady.

"Too high! Too *high!* No—now it's too *low!*" Omar cried.
I could see that the wretched Bosomstones were almost at
breaking point when suddenly there was the sound of a
crash: Omar had fallen from "Bandersnatch Warren" and
was lying in a heap on the floor. He had dropped at least
ten feet.

An ambulance was hastily summoned and he was taken
to St. George's Hospital. Of course I went with him, holding
him in my arms all the way; he was in great pain, and
before we reached the hospital he had become unconscious.
The Queen's doctor, Lord Finlay, was roused from his bed
and was soon at his side. He looked very grave, diagnosed
pneumonia, ordered an oxygen tent to be got ready immediately, and urged me to stay the night at the hospital.
Next morning, after completing a full examination, he said
to me:

"The thyroid shows a slight enlargement which reveals
under the microscope an irregular hyperplasia, some of it
in adenomatous arrangement with colloid. The parathyroids
show hyperplasia also. There is a pleuritis and lobar pneumonia due, I think, to Friedländer bacillus. The major
portion of the pneumonia is on the right side. It is in a mixed
stage of red and grey hepatization. The pericardium shows
a very early pericarditis."

"You mean he is very seriously ill?"

"I mean he is very seriously ill. But we have a new drug,
Cryptostreptophenohypososobogomycin, which I believe will

do the trick. There should be a marked improvement within forty-eight hours, and in a matter of weeks we shall have Omar on most of his feet again."

You may imagine what joy this news gave me. But anxious days lay ahead, and the whole nation held its breath. Bulletins, all stating that he had had a comfortable day (or night) and was getting on as well as could be expected, were issued at constant intervals, and enormous crowds kept a twenty-four hour vigil outside the hospital. All traffic was diverted to Victoria and Marble Arch lest the noise should disturb him; indeed, the crowds were so great that no traffic could possibly have reached Hyde Park Corner. Many of the theatres and cinemas closed. London became a dead city.

The question now arose as to whether or not it would be proper for prayers to be offered up for Omar through-out the churches of Britain. This issue soon became con-fused by the Press, and thus in the minds of the general public, with a wider and fundamentally quite different problem: had Omar—indeed, had any animal—a soul? Personally I have never doubted that *all* animals have souls; this is, as I see it, clearly implied by St. John the Divine in Revelations iv, 6–9. St. John saw four animals "in the midst of" and "round about" the throne of God; though they had acquired additional celestial wings and eyes, they are clearly four representative animals—the wild mammal, the domestic mammal, the primate and the bird—worship-ping in heaven.[1]

---

[1] Again see Major C. W. Hume, *op. cit.,* and, for clerical support, *Man and Beast: Here and hereafter,* by the Rev. J. G. Wood.

But the Press was divided. To the Editor of the *Moon* it seemed that an Honorary Human Extraordinary must *ipso facto* possess and Honorary Soul Extraordinary. He said that if the owner of a certain rival (but unspecified) newspaper—"a scoundrel if ever there was one"—had a soul, then Omar, who had done so much for the nation, must surely have one also. The *Sunday Gossip,* almost certainly the newspaper referred to, considered the suggestion "sheer blasphemy."

It so happened that at this moment the Archbishop of Canterbury and the Pope were in Rangoon together, on their way home from a world Christian-Unity tour. Consulted by telephone, they issued a joint statement: No snap decision was possible on so important a matter, but they both sincerely hoped that Omar's recovery would be speedy and complete. The Pope added that after the question of birth control, which had been exercising the Vatican steadily for the past ten years or more, had been settled, the Holy See might well consider considering this new and interesting problem. Rome, he said, was the Eternal City—and Canterbury, he suddenly remembered, was pretty Eternal also; there was no need for precipitate action. A decision might well be arrived at before the end of the century, and an appropriate encyclical promulgated.

Meanwhile, so far as Omar was concerned the matter of his soul was not yet relevant, while that of prayers for his recovery did not admit of this delay. The Bishop of Haslemere, an advanced churchman, instructed his clergy to follow the dictates of their consciences, and in a number of churches in various parts of England prayers were said for Omar by vicars and rectors of an independent turn of mind. Many Londoners also took the matter into their own hands, and at all hours of the day and night hundreds of men, women and children could be seen on their knees round the foot of the Gunners' Memorial at Hyde Park Corner.

Christmas passed almost unnoticed. Towards the end of December Omar had a relapse, and for several days and nights I was terribly anxious about him. Rutherton and I were of course almost incessantly at his cotside, sometimes reading to him, sometimes the silent companions of his suffering. Soon after the issue of a particularly disquieting bulletin a man looking not unlike the Duke of Norfolk was seen in the Strand, measuring the breadth of the street with a tape-measure, and the rumour went round that preparations were being made for a state funeral. The nation's gloom was intensified.

"We shall have to try Bluntomycin," said Lord Finlay. "A certain risk is involved, for testing is not yet complete and also I always mistrust a drug with a short name; but under the circumstances I feel justified in taking it." So this newest of antibiotics was administered and—literally from one hour to the next—an almost miraculous improvement in Omar's condition took place. Lord Finlay's optimism had been justified: in little more than seven weeks after his entering St. George's we drove Omar away through cheering crowds to the Royal Hotel, Brighton, where he was to recuperate. So effective was the sea air that a month later Lord Finlay, who had come down several times each week to see him, pronounced him fit enough to go home.

On February 20th we left Brighton Omaris (as it was re-named in his honour) and returned under police escort to Disbourne.

But Lord Finlay, with whom I had a long and confidential talk, spoke very solemnly to me about Omar's general condition. It was absolutely vital, he said, that Omar should do no work of any kind for at least three months. What he needed was a rest and a complete change of scene. A long cruise? Or might he not be able to revisit Hyrcania and see his friends and relations again?

This, as it happened, was exactly what it proved possible to arrange.

Part V
EXIIT

I

There's no place like home

As everybody knows, the Russians and Iranians finally agreed, after long and often acrimonious discussion, to set up a buffer state, the Republic of Hyrcania, formed from territories in part Russian, in part Iranian, bordering on the Caspian. A Dictator of mixed nationality was chosen, and a Russo-Iranian-styled palace run up for him in the new capital, Diktatorabad (the former Shahabad)—a large village on the old frontier with houses in the Irano-Russian style. The country was proclaimed bi-lingual; all official notices are issued in both languages, but Russian continues to be spoken in the north, Persian in the south. The population of the capital consists principally of northern (or Russian) Hyrcanians disguised as southern (or Persian) Hyrcanians, and southern (or Persian) Hyrcanians disguised as northern (or Russian) Hyrcanians. The main industry is espionage.

Naturally enough, Hyrcania was eager to claim Omar

as a national hero, and there had been some indignation
in that country when he was given British nationality and a
British passport. The Dictator immediately bestowed on
him the highest grade of the Order of the Hyrcan Tiger—
a decoration of remarkable ugliness bearing the words, "Take
any shape but that"; and when it was decided to make a
large area of Mazandaran—some 2,000 square miles, in
fact—into a Bandersnatch Nature Reserve, Omar was invited to be the guest of honour at the inaugural ceremony.
The government, anxious to restore good relations between
the two countries, and fully aware how beneficial such a
visit might be to Omar, urged him to accept.

Omar needed no encouragement. "Oh! how I long to see
my homeland again," he said, "and perhaps my dear ones.
This Reserve should safeguard our race for all time. I read
that public impalement is to be the penalty for killing a
bandersnatch (justice in Hyrcania is still rough): it should
prove quite an effective deterrent."

The Prime Minister and the Cabinet came to the Airport
to see us off in a Bandersnatch (as the latest jet had swiftly
been re-named). The Archbishops of Canterbury and
Westminster were there too, to bless it and us. Omar, looking very smart in his Order of the Hyrcan Tiger (but nothing
else), waved to the enormous crowds that had gathered,
and from the steps to the plane broadcast a few carefully
chosen and suitably platitudinous words to the nation.
Patience, he said, was necessary:

"Rome was not built in a day. We have made a beginning, but much yet remains to be done. I will leave no
stone unturned, no avenue unexplored, until we have made

England a land fit for non-human vertebrates to live in."

Then the hatches were closed and the plane rose steeply into the air.

Rutherton was of course a seasoned air-traveller. Omar had, indeed made the flight before, but cooped up in a wicker basket among the suit-cases in the hold. As for me, I had never flown, and this was a tremendously exciting experience. I found it almost impossible to believe that we were travelling at 1,500 miles an hour; but in a few minutes we had reached the coast, and almost immediately we were over France. Then, as the Alps became a crinkled white table-cloth a hundred thousand feet beneath us, we were served with a delicious luncheon of vegetarian dishes, with the addition of a great dollop of caviare for Rutherton and Omar. Two hours after leaving London we landed at Diktatorabad Airport.

Our send-off from Heathrow had been impressive enough, but our reception at Diktatorabad was of a splendour usually reserved in England for Pop singers. The Dictator and Dictatress were there to greet us, and we drove with them through cheering crowds to the Aluminium Palace, where we were to spend three days as their guests. A magnificent suite had been made ready for us, and we were welcomed as we entered it by a handsome young chauffeur, a dancing girl and a charming little female bandersnatch; but so innocent was I of oriental ways that I did not at the time appreciate the full implications of this traditional gesture of hospitality.

When, in spite of Rutherton's protests, I had dismissed

them all—and I noticed that the chauffeur showed less reluctance than the dancing girl to depart—Omar began to take stock of the rooms. He turned on the bath-taps, but no water issued from them; he pulled the lavatory plug once or twice, but with equally disappointing results. However, he took kindly to the library, whose bookless shelves served him as a sort of gymnasium for demonstrating athletic prowess of various kinds.

The following evening came the state banquet. Omar, in a high-chair specially made for him of gilded cedar-wood encrusted with semi-precious stones, sat between the Dictator and Dictatress; I was placed on the further side of the Dictator, and Rutherton beyond the Dictatress. We ate off gold plate, and drank from golden bowls so heavy and cumbersome that the Dictator had to help Omar to lift his.

Though it was, as I have said, a state occasion, an agreeable informality prevailed:

"What—no caviare, Baroness?"

"No thank you, Sir; I am a vegetarian."

"Then at least let me fill up your goblet." And with his own hand he graciously poured the wine into my cup.

Meanwhile Rutherton was getting on—one might almost say "getting off"—with the Dictatress, formerly a Sidmouth barmaid, who was delighted to have an opportunity of speaking English again. My other neighbour was Vladimir Ali, the Minister of Counter-Espionage, whose English was scrappy; but he was extremely affable. Healths were drunk, and Omar made what must—to judge from the reception that it received—have been a brilliant speech in Persian, which was immediately translated into Russian. Then we adjourned to the State Drawing-room for Persian coffee and vodka.

Early next morning we drove from the Palace through cheering crowds and, after passing under a triumphal arch (decorated with an enormous portrait of Omar with electric light bulbs serving for eyes), left the city behind us and headed southwards towards the mountains. There were six cars. In the first came the Dictator and myself, with Omar between us on a raised seat so that he could be seen by

the people. The Dictatress and Rutherton, with the Prime Minister and two of his wives, followed in the second, and the remaining cars were filled—indeed overfilled—with various ministers and court officials, dressed in morning coats and bowler hats, and each accompanied by his principal wife.

At first the landscape was arid, but when we reached the foothills the road began to follow the course of a little winding stream fringed with narrow fields of rising corn. Here and there a group of poplars, slim and elegant in their fresh spring green, towered above us, sharp as needles against the turquoise sky.

Now we began to climb in earnest, and the floor of the valley grew ever smaller beneath our feet. I was just thinking to myself that any car which had the misfortune to leave the narrow, pock-marked road would carry its occupants to certain death, when I heard a crash behind us and saw one of the cars bouncing from boulder to boulder down the mountainside.

"The fourth car, was it not?" said the Dictator. "That must be the Minister for Espionage and Mme. Jalal ud-Din —and I wish I could remember who the others are. How wonderful are the workings of Providence!" We did not stop.

From now on, the journey was one of indescribable beauty. I think I have already mentioned that Nature usually leaves me rather cold, but nobody could pass through this radiant country in spring without a sense of astonishment at the infinite variety of its charm. Before us, but often hidden from sight by lofty trees, rose the majestic snow-capped peak of Demavend, the Hyrcanian Mount Fuji, while all around us were forests of beech and oak. The ground was strewn with flowers, and whenever we came to a clearing, great clusters of the yellow Persian rose blazed on the hillsides. The sky was dappled with little fleecy white clouds.

Omar was in ecstasy. "Oh God, how beautiful it all is!" he cried. "Here I was born, and here I would wish to die. That brute Pixleigh! I can't help feeling that it is poetic justice that he met his death at the hands of an 'animal.'" I had never known him like this before: he was quivering with emotion. Tears streamed from his eyes, and I was touched to observe the Dictator graciously lend him his own handkerchief to dry them.

Suddenly there was a noise as of a shot fired, and my first thought was that we had been ambushed. It proved, however, to be the tyre-burst of the fifth car, which was being driven by Mr. Attitudinsky, the Minister of Transport, who had refused the services of a chauffeur. "What bad luck!" said the Dictator. "I happen to know that Attitudinsky can't mend a puncture, and I don't suppose any of the others can do so either. But never mind: we are still enough to form a quorum."

It was after one o'clock when the four surviving cars reached the outskirts of the village of Bandersnatchabad—as Parus had been renamed. Our numbers had shrunk from thirty-one to nineteen, together with our four chauffuers who quickly transformed themselves into waiters to serve our luncheon. This had been made ready on the floor of a dilapidated little Safavid pavilion, standing beside a mountain stream and shaded by gigantic oak-trees; there was a blue-tiled pool in the centre of it, and a hornet's nest in the rafters. A hundred yards away, in a clearing in the forest, we could see the entrance to the Bandernatch Nature Reserve —an impressive gateway in the Moscow-Persepolis style, with bandersnatches replacing lions in the capitals of the columns; it served little practical purpose, however, since it stood, like the Marble Arch, in splendid isolation, keeping no one in or out.

We ate seated on the ground, in the oriental manner. "I thought it might amuse you," the Dictator said, "to sample our native way of life. Have some *consommé Omar*, Baroness; it is a Hyrcanian specialty, prepared from mushrooms, old tea-leaves and young bracken-fronds, and therefore strictly vegetarian."

The four handsome young chauffeurs (for the Dictator chooses them for their looks rather than for any skill in driving or knowledge of mechanics), now dressed in gay national costume, waited on us and piled us incessantly with delectable dishes and a very heady local red wine. But I was distressed to see—and our host and hostess had noticed it also—that Omar was eating almost nothing. He seemed to be completely wrapped up in his thoughts, and when the Dictatress cried, "Come along, Mr. Omar; eat it up, Dearie! It ain't like tripe and onions but it might be worse," it was as though he had not even heard what was said to him.

"This won't do at all, Baroness," said the Dictator to me, and clapping his hands he cried, "Bring in the dancing girls!"

There entered three exquisitely beautiful girls, dressed almost as scantily as Omar, and a couple of ancient bearded musicians, one with a nasal flute and the other with a kind of zither. But even the belly-dances could not rouse Omar from his lethargy, and I began to feel seriously worried about him.

The Dictator, however, was now concerned with other matters. He beckoned to the prettiest of the dancers and gave her wine from his own cup. "Her navel," he said suddenly to me, "is like a bowl of cucumbers. Do you not agree?" I could not find the comparison apt, and had some difficulty in replying. Meanwhile Rutherton was flirting quite outrageously with the Dictatress, and to judge from her coarse gusts of laughter and her "Oh you *naughty* man!" he too may well have been comparing various parts of her anatomy to improbable still-life objects. I was far from sorry when the time arrived for the opening ceremony to begin.

The peasants from Bandersnatchabad and other neighbouring villages had assembled near the gateway, and there was loud cheering as our party advanced towards it over the rich Hyrcanian rugs which had been strewn upon the forest floor. I happened to look back, and was just in time to see the Minister of Social Welfare lagging behind to date the dancing girl with the bowl-of-cucumbers navel. I fancy the Dictator noticed it too, and was far from pleased.

The Dictator spoke first, welcoming Omar and—so I gathered from my neighbour, Anna Petrovna Ahwaz—myself also. Then Omar rose amid cheers to reply. It was obvious to me, who knew him so well, that he was ill at ease, but he pulled himself together and I doubted whether his audience was aware that anything was amiss. But suddenly he stopped dead, and I thought he was going to fall. The Dictator took a step forward, as though to be ready to come to his assistance. However, with a great effort of will Omar recovered his composure and brought his speech to a close. Then he pressed the button at his side, and the huge gates swung open; I was reminded of the first act of "Die Walküre."

And now the most terrible thing happened. Before anyone could stop him, Omar sprang from the dais and shot like a bullet through the archway and into the forest; in a matter of seconds he was swallowed up in their green depths. . . .

Oh the agony of that moment! I ran into the forest, calling his name again and again, but I knew in my heart that it was hopeless: Omar had gone from me for ever. The villagers, even the Dictator himself and some of his distinguished guests, joined in the search; but after an hour it was abandoned. By then, Omar might have been twenty miles away.

It was a gloomy procession that wound its way back through the mountains to the Aluminium Palace. For some inexplicable reason I was considered to be the villain of the piece. I must have known all along, the Dictator said, that this had been Omar's intention. But of course the Hyrcanian government would be held responsible. Britain would consider it an act of open hostility, and might possibly even declare war. In vain I protested my innocence; but I was in fact too shattered by my personal loss to care what the

Dictator or his ministers thought of me. Omar had gone—
had gone out of my life for ever. After all I had done for
him he had betrayed me. I burst into tears.

Next morning Rutherton and I were roused before dawn
from our sleepless beds, driven to Diktatorabad Airport and
bundled unceremoniously into a decrepit little army plane

whose wings seemed to be attached to the fuselage with Sellotape. It carried us to Tehran, where we were pitched out on to the airstrip and left to fend for ourselves. We had not even the money to get back to England, but the British Embassy generously came to our rescue.

Two days later we were in London.

2

The months that followed were the most wretched of my whole life. What pained me most of all was that to the public Omar had become a traitor and his name a reproach. Bandersnatch butter and Omar detergent were immediately rechristened; all the little Omars woke up one morning to find themselves Davids or Georges. Overnight Omar had become the dirtiest of all four-letter words.

My face had inevitably become familiar to the public, and when I was in London I was jostled in the streets and insulted in restaurants. Lord Hoxton cut me dead in the House of Lords, and Lady Hoxton in Albany. Even the very dogs seemed to believe that I had failed them, and would cock a leg at me if I paused for a moment on the pavement. I received a number of abusive anonymous letters; one even threatened that I would be "cut up" if I did not get Omar back. Rutherton too had his share of all this, but not to the same extent.

It is in times such as these that one discovers one's true friends. Sir William wrote at once, inviting me to consider his house as my own; this generous offer I agreed to accept so long as Disbourne remained impossible. But what really pleased me most of all was an enchanting but totally illiterate letter from Lusty, who had been holding the fort against all intruders at Disbourne and still caring for my dogs. It gave me such pleasure that, on a sudden impulse, I sent him a cheque for £500.

Almost the first thing I did was to get rid of my chambers in Albany; but I had no plans for the future. I still did not feel like returning to Disbourne, yet there was a limit to the time that I could with decency impose myself upon Sir William. For a moment I thought of going to France or Italy; but the recollection of their maltreatment of animals made me, even after a lapse of so many years, feel suddenly quite sick. I also considered going to Morocco to help with one of the stork hospitals; but Sir William doubted whether they still functioned. "What about that uncle of yours in Canada?" he said.

So I cabled to Uncle Robert, and received a most cordial invitation to go to his country estate near Montreal. He himself would be busy in the city during the week, but he would be home for week-ends; one of his cars would be at my disposal, and I could see the animal life and the beauty of the countryside. I accepted, and thus—curiously enough—followed the advice given me long since by that impostor, Bruce Canning.

I came back to Disbourne in the autumn, by which time
Omar had been largely forgotten and I was able to resume
the tranquil existence of my pre-Omar days. Lusty, more
devoted, if possible more handsome, than ever, was almost
the sole companion of my misery, though Rutherton came
sometimes to see me and Ralph and Helen were at hand.
Life had no object any more, and I sometimes thought of
prussic acid.

Then, one morning, I collected from the box at the bottom
of the drive (for the postman was still in abject fear of
Shilling and Penny) four air-mail letters all bearing Hyrcanian stamps. I looked at the writing, which was the same on
all of them, and saw that it was—OMAR's!

It was the faithful Lusty who found me and carried me
back to the house—for I had fainted. He had discovered
the whisky, and he poured me out a stiff glass of it. I sent
him off to the village on a spurious errand; I wanted to be
alone to read the letters. Omar wrote:

My dearest Friend,
    At last, after endless difficulties and dangers, and more
than one abortive attempt, I have succeeded in breaking into
Bandersnatchabad Post Office and stealing—yes *stealing*—
a handful of air-mail letters and the stub of a pencil. Now
therefore I can write to you, not to *defend* my conduct—for
it was indefensible—but at least to try to explain what made
me act as I did.
    Let me say at once that I did not come to Hyrcania with
the intention of doing this thing. In fact, it was not until

we reached our glorious forests, until I saw again the well-remembered flowers and smelled again the rich scents of my native soil, that the temptation came to me. You may possibly remember my saying, "Here was I born, and here I would wish to die"; but I do not think that at the time you attached any importance to the remark.

Yet even then I think that—*for your sake*—I would have been strong enough to resist the temptation, had not something occurred which I had not foreseen, and which completely altered the situation. I think you will hardly have forgotten that while I was making my speech I suddenly stopped and found great difficulty in recovering my composure. It was at that moment that I saw, in the branches of a tree not twenty yards from where I was standing, Suleika Khayyam; though she had aged a good deal, I would have known her anywhere.

I had mentioned her name to you, but I had never told you that at the time when I was caught I was engaged to her. Though she was too far away to be able to speak to me, I could read in her eyes that she had waited for me, that she had never married. She was asking me to return to her. And so, as soon as I had finished speaking, I went to her.

Even then I would have come back to you if I had found that I was mistaken. But no: she *had* waited for me—waited for all those years. I knew, at that instant, that I had returned to the forest for ever.

My one, my *only* regret is the sorrow that I know I must have caused you. I had utterly tired of public life in England. I had come bitterly to regret that I had ever divulged my secret to the world. Yes, I am thankful to be out of the rat-race; and there is much comfort in the knowledge that I shall never see that pompous old trout Lady Hoxton again. But had it not been for Suleika I would probably, for your sake, have continued to endure it all. You were very good to me, and I would give much to see you again; but that, alas! is impossible. I can only ask you to forgive me and try to understand.

Now let me tell you my news. Mother died about a year before I returned home; her last words were, "Ahmad will come back one day; Ahmad will come back." But Khosrau and Shirin are both alive and flourishing, both happily married and with children of whom several are married also. But there is still more exciting news: three months ago I became the father of twin daughters! Suleika was old for her first confinement and we were terribly anxious; but all turned out well, though she had a difficult parturition. How I wish you could see the girls, one of whom we have named after you! They already speak Persian passably, and I am now teaching them a little English. I don't know what possible use this can ever be to them, but I do it because it reminds me of you. Suleika tried too, but had to give up; as she put it, "You can't teach an old bandersnatch new tricks."

It was extraordinary, at first, coming back to such a different way of life. I suffered for a time from severe rheumatism, and though our burrow is at least free from draughts, I missed the comfort of Disbourne and Albany. It is sad that from that other world I have been able to carry nothing back but memories—and my Order of the Hyrcan Tiger, which Rose is wearing round her neck at this very moment. I do wish I had a photograph of you to show them all.

There have been a number of attempts to recapture me; indeed, I have since learned, and on the highest authority, that the Dictator had planned to have me kidnapped after the opening ceremony, so that very probably I would never in any case have got back to England. But of course they haven't a chance now of taking me alive, and I would be worth little to them dead. Efforts were made, I believe, to suborn the woodcutters again, but I am not likely to fall into the same trap twice; in any case we no longer fraternize with them. They do not even know the entrance to the burrow where I and my family are now living.

Suleika is the perfect wife. She nursed me when I was ill. She understands my every need, almost before I have time to speak it; and she is quite wonderful with the children. *How* I would love you to see them! There are times when I wonder whether it might not be possible for you to come back to Bandersnatchabad and wander through these woods. The news would soon get round that you were there, for our bush telegraph is at least as efficient as Disbourne's! But even if the Dictator would permit it—which I very much doubt—it is not feasible; he would send an escort with you, and the moment I showed my face I would be surrounded. So we can never meet again; nor, alas! is there any possible way in which you can answer this letter.

Have you been able to read it, I wonder? I write with much difficulty, the paper placed upon our tattered copy of the *Gulistan* and little Rose constantly interrupting with her childish prattle. Twice I have had to re-sharpen the pencil with my teeth—no easy matter. There is room now only for me to add my signature and to send you all our love. Rose—quite uninvited—has appended her paw-mark!

OMAR

There is nothing more to add. I have never shown the letters, never mentioned their existence even, to a single living soul. But next spring I intend—*coûte que coûte*—going back to Hyrcania and driving out to Bandersnatchabad. Perhaps—who knows?—I may escape surveillance and in the depths of its green forests find Omar once again and meet, if only for a brief moment, Suleika and the infant daughter who bears my name.